Dear Allyson,

Truth is truth,

Be Well, courtenay.

20

From Health Heretic

To

Common Law Advocate

By

courtenay-adam-lawrence :heading

ISBN Number: 9781527256521

Paperback edition (2020)

To judy: the true definition of unconditional love

(and remember, the first forty years are always the worst.)

Warning and thanks

The most difficult subjects can be explained to the most slow-witted man if he has not formed any idea of them already; but the simplest thing cannot be made clear to the most intelligent man if he is firmly persuaded that he knows already, without a shadow of doubt, what is laid before him.
Leo Tolstoi

I am not a doctor; I am not a lawyer.

I do know a lot of things about a lot of disparate things.

I know a lot of people who know a lot of things about a lot of things.

I know a lot of people who know a lot of things about a few things.

I know a lot of people who are incredibly intelligent, talented, kind and generous.

I have the privilege and am extremely grateful to call many of these people friends.

In this book I do mention a number of these friends, who happen to be eminent individuals in their respective professions.

There are so many others who I do not name, but who have helped encourage and shape me into the man I am today.

I am truly grateful to you all.

In short, I am blessed to have a veritable network of wonderful people working, in their own ways, to help humanity.

I love connecting people for their mutual benefit.

I also love connecting the dots...

As I say, I am not a doctor but there are many who are and who have already woken up to the ills of the current medical system.

A growing number have spoken out (at great personal cost to themselves and their families) and continue to do so in order to uphold the ethics of the profession; these ethics include:

The respect for autonomy - where the patient has the right to refuse or choose their treatment;

Non-maleficence - to not be the cause of harm; and

Beneficence - to act in the best interest of the patient.

The following testimonies are from just three such Doctors, each one of whom is a shining light in a world of increasing darkness:

Back in 2018 I thought the IOM was the (US) Institute Of Medicine. But in December 2018, I had visited the IOM and realized those initials also stand for the Isle of Man, a small country located in the middle of the Irish Sea. I gave a presentation on the fraudulent trials and hidden dangers of the human papilloma virus (HPV) vaccine, most commonly referred to as Gardasil. I met with a small group of the Isle of Man's concerned citizens. They have grown from a few voices in the wilderness to among the most knowledgeable and powerful leaders in the world, loudly decrying vaccination as a global disaster.

Early in my career, I was a board-certified Emergency Medicine Physician and Director of a Level II trauma center for nearly 12 years. In 1996 I moved to Cleveland, Ohio and opened an integrative medicine practice which I am proud to say has served patients from all 50 States and 17 foreign countries. And then, serendipitously I attended a four-day conference hosted by the National Vaccine Information Center (NVIC) in Washington, DC in September 2000; it's hard to believe that was nearly twenty years ago. There were at least 700 people in attendance: activists, physicians, lawyers, researchers and people with their vaccine injured children in wheelchairs. I'd been in medicine for 15 years at that time and as I looked across the room thought to myself, "How did I miss all this?". I had grown up in a three-generation chiropractic family. I was not vaccinated as a child nor were any of my cousins or any of their family. So a harmful event from a vaccine was never on my radar.

I had age appropriate measles, mumps, rubella, and chickenpox. I had pertussis (whooping cough) twice. I am now in my 60s and, like many baby boomers, we remember those childhood infections. We lived through them and no one died. We get so terrorised over the childhood illnesses. We need to start calling them what they are - infections - instead of calling them diseases. An infection comes and goes rather quickly in the vast majority of those who contract the illness. A disease is a chronic condition, such as insulin-dependent diabetes, or a seizure disorder or an autoimmune illness. If we understood the role of infection in a person's life, and the importance of fever, perhaps we would think differently regarding the necessity of vaccines.

After attending the NVIC Conference, I was launched on a quest to thoroughly investigate vaccines and what the act of vaccinating actually did to the body. I studied the illustrious mainstream medical journals, including Vaccine, The Pediatric Infectious Disease Journal, JAMA, the New England Journal of Medicine and many others. The more I read, the more disturbing the information became. How could physicians simply deny the studies in their own journals that were chronicling the carnage being done to children - and adults - but which was coming through that needle. The more I read, the late-night hours became an addiction. I kept thinking I was missing something. Deeper down the rabbit hole I went and the information became more and more disturbing.

Surely, if people just knew how vile the stuff was that came out of that vial they would just stop vaccinating. They would run in the opposite direction like the TV cartoon, the 'Road Runner'. The industry would almost instantly implode. Once people knew that vaccines contained cells from aborted fetal tissue, aluminium and mercury, several known carcinogens and stray viruses that can cause cancer, they would stop injecting these slurries into their children.

Well, twenty years later we have more vaccines than ever. We now also have mandatory vaccination being pushed through to take away our rights. Mandatory vaccination is a violation of the Nuremberg Codes, the Declaration of Helsinki and the ground work established by the International Medical Society. We are all genetically unique individuals. And every vaccine that contains animal matter - fetal bovine serum, chicken fibroblasts, egg particles and more - is an experiment. We must retain our right to refuse by declaring the separation between me and my government is at the level of my skin.

In July 2019, I again visited the Isle of Man for the international Tynwald Day. My visit was disrupted by the unscripted arrest of my host. Likely, wearing a yellow vest carrying the names of two youngsters who died after receiving the HPV (Gardasil) vaccination was unconnected with police incarceration.

For all that, this lovely small Island could yet learn that truth is a currency. I welcome the discussion and progress towards Common Law remedies, a subject for which my late-husband had a great affinity. With luck, those who independently examine medicine and the law will often find it is not at all what they think.

Dr Sherri Tenpenny.

<↓> <↓> <↓>

As medical students we were all taught that people stopped dying from infectious disease because of vaccines. There were other diseases for which the death rates also plummeted, such as typhoid, cholera, scarlet fever, rheumatic fever, pneumonia, meningitis and many more, but we were told this was due to better social conditions.

With the information overload during medical training no-one stopped to ask, "If people stopped dying from these diseases because of hygiene, how do we know that people didn't stop dying from all infectious diseases because of 'hygiene'?" We just accepted it. One set in the 'vaccine-preventable' box and the other in the 'hygiene-preventable' box.

And so it continued.

In the 1980's when working in community paediatrics I used to counsel parents who did not want their baby to have the whooping cough vaccine after studies were published suggesting that some children had become brain damaged or had died after receiving it. I used to tell them, "We are told that the chance of your baby dying or being brain damaged from the disease is ten times higher than the chance of any bad reaction from the vaccines. Any sensible, responsible, parent would accept the vaccine.".

My own children were born in the early 1990's and I unhesitatingly had them vaccinated with what was then available; far less than now. I even let my elder daughter be given an out-of-date BCG vaccine (I had noticed the expired date on the vial but was told it was fine). She had a terrible fever, screaming and severe distress for hours yet I still continued with the rest; so great was my faith that vaccines were safe, effective, a miracle of modern medicine and there was no alternative. That is what all doctors think. Unless they wake up and do their own research.

10

My 'wake-up' call was the measles rubella campaign of 1994. The Chief Medical officer told all medical personnel that even two shots of the - what was then a 'one shot for life' - measles vaccine would not necessarily protect people from measles when the epidemic came; they would need a third. So you could have the vaccine twice, with all the unquantified risk of adverse reactions, and still get the disease with all the risks associated with that. I realised that what I had learned about vaccines and had been telling patients was not correct. I had been given, and was giving, wrong information.

As part of my search for information and being unable to find reliable data from the Department of Health about disease incidence and deaths before the 1940's for most of the diseases against which we vaccinate, I ended up having to go to the Office for National Statistics myself; taking off the shelf the musty old books from the mid nineteenth century when theses statistics started to be collected, and drawing my own graphs to see what was going on.

I was shocked to find that over 95% of the reduction in deaths from diseases such as measles and whooping cough occurred before there was any vaccine and before even antibiotics were available. It was undoubtedly a miracle but it wasn't due to vaccines. So what was it due to?

This started a long journey to find out what health is - certainly not what I had been taught in medical school - and why we get disease. I have read thousands of scientific studies, papers and journals over the last 27 years, as well as studying homeopathy, naturopathy, the philosophy of natural hygiene, nutritional and other spiritual and lifestyle factors that determine real health - which is more than just the absence of disease - and educating myself on how to respect and work with the innate intelligence of the body rather than against it.

Acquiring the knowledge and putting it into practice has been of great benefit to myself, my patients and my family. Other parts of this journey, however, have been at great personal cost.

Once you step out of the box you become a target.

Agreeing to be an expert witness in a legal case where two absent fathers wanted to force vaccination on their unvaccinated children against the mothers' wishes led to three years of hell for me and my family. The judge preferred the mostly unreferenced opinions of the two experts on the Joint Committee on Vaccination and Immunisation to my fully referenced report, which an Appeal Judge called 'junk science.' The UK General Medical Council then accused me of serious professional misconduct in a bid to strike me off the medical register so I would not be able to practice medicine, and my defence organisation said, at the eleventh hour, that I didn't have a case and should plead guilty.

I managed to find my own lawyer to take over the case. He devised a strategy, instructed a barrister and defended my case to the hilt. At a three week hearing, three years after first being accused, the panel completely exonerated me.

My family and I never regained the lost years.

As a child at school, less than twenty years after the Second World War against totalitarianism, I was taught to be proud of living in a democracy, a free society; to remember the men and women who gave up their lives so we could have freedom of thought, freedom of speech, freedom of expression, freedom of association, the right to governance of our own bodies and that of our children; a free press to protect us from the excesses of overweening government and powerful corporations.

75 years on these rights are being steadily and relentlessly

eroded and the press who should be protecting us are their henchmen.

It is good that there are people like Courtenay, of Jurby Wellness, challenging this dangerous situation, educating themselves and other people about wellness and who are fighting to defend our common law rights.

Dr Jayne LM Donegan
MBBS DRCOG DCH DFFP MRCGP MFHom HMA
02 March 2020

⟨⟩ ⟨⟩ ⟨⟩

In 1980, I was finishing my studies: a major in chemistry and a specialization in biology at the University of Virginia. This is significant because only 40 years ago there was not even a degree program in biochemistry. It was there that I first encountered a misogynist. An assistant professor voiced his objective to give failing grades to female premed students as he believed women should not attend medical school. Most of my female classmates simply avoided his classes but my degree program required three classes taught by this professor. Naive and fueled by my passion for natural products chemistry I persisted. My poor grades in two of these classes made it clear by my third year that I would not have the grades to go to medical school. In fact, I struggled to keep the grade point average necessary to keep my scholarships.

The last class of my senior year was a biochemistry lab class required for all premed students, approximately 500 in total. In a lab, I was home. I am a lab rat. For my lab reports, I received the highest grade of all 500 students. To my horror, the final exam contained not questions about biochemistry labs but the type of advanced organic chemistry questions, which I had failed previously. I received the worst grade on that exam of all 500 students and instead of the A+ I had earned, I was given an A- in the class. I protested to the dean of students who was sympathetic, but because others had improved their grades granting them entrance into medical school, he could do nothing but reprimand the professor and in future make it a requirement that final exams be given only on the subject matter of the class. Wasn't that the requirement all along? I remember the day as if it was yesterday. I almost quit school only weeks before graduation on the principle. I thank God for my friend Katie, who talked sense into me as I sat sobbing on the lawn in front of the rotunda wondering what happened to Thomas Jefferson's principles. Apparently, they did not apply to women.

March 31, 1980 as I wondered what kind of job I would get

14

being offered only jobs in the petroleum industry, I saw the cover of Time magazine. It showed a droplet from a hypodermic needle and the words "INTERFERON: The IF for cancer. I knew immediately what I wanted to do. The National Cancer Institute (NCI) advertised in the Washington Post for a protein chemist to purify interferon over memorial-day weekend only a week after graduation. I applied and on June 10, 1980 I started my dream career, first purifying interferon at the NCI facility at FT. Detrick in Frederick, Maryland.

Every step of the way I encountered misogyny and corruption. I accepted the job. The male chemist was leaving to attend medical school. After I started the job I received the formal letter stating that the technician job would pay not the $15,000 the male technician was paid but only $10,000. I vehemently protested but to no avail. I was told the man had a family and that was why he was paid more for the same job. I kept working anyway because I did not care about money, I was in heaven. We made the first interferon given to cancer patients and some were doing very well. We also purified many cancer drugs from plants. I naively thought I'd spend a few years making drugs and maybe then get an opportunity to go to medical school.

The events of 1982 would end that dream for me forever as the first human disease causing retrovirus was isolated and my team would be assigned to purify very large quantities of the virus, growing the virus in a 200 liter fermentor in the human cell line, HUT-102. The problem was no one knew anything about the transmission of the virus and the personnel were not provided any kind of safety precautions or training.

Even more alarming to my supervisor and me, several of the female technicians were pregnant. We wrote a formal letter saying we could not complete the job without adequate safety precautions and a few weeks later I received a letter stating that my position had been eliminated. That is, that the NCI no longer needed a protein chemist. They did not fire me, they simply said my position was part of a reduction in force.

Devastated but not giving up, I attended a seminar about immune modulator proteins called cytokines and learned a new program called the biological response modifiers program was being started to develop cytokines as therapeutics for cancer. This was the first translational research program in the country. I approached the scientist giving the seminar and asked if the program needed a protein chemist. I naively told him I thought those cytokines might be important and we could cure cancer. Fortunately, he did not laugh but invited me to his office to talk. After a wonderful discussion, he told me of an investigator who needed a technician and arranged an interview with Dr. Frank Ruscetti. The interview was vintage Frank.

He said, "I see from your CV that you purified Interleukin 2 and HTLV-1." I said, "Yes". He said, "So I suppose you read the literature about them?" I said, "Of course". He asked me to tell him who wrote the papers. I said I did not know, as it did not matter to me who wrote the papers. Wrong answer. He said I DID. I thought, 'Well that is the end of that job!' and proceeded to talk about the Boston Celtics as there was a poster of Bill Russel and Larry Bird on his wall. I left a few minutes later discouraged to learn later that I had gotten the job! But not for the reason I thought. I got the job because the hiring manager for the contractor told Frank I was a trouble maker and he could not hire me. He inquired why I was considered a trouble maker. She replied, "She asks too many questions!" He screamed, "She is a scientist. She is supposed to ask questions! You hire her or I'll have you fired".

That started a 37-year collaboration with Frank, a scientist of total integrity, an oasis in the middle of a plague of corruption that we only learned the depth of in the past decade of persecution and cover-up by every level of the U.S. federal government: the NIH, FDA, CDC in collusion with the WHO, which started with the realization that our isolation of a new family of mouse retroviruses from patients with ME/CFS and cancers and the strong association with many diseases.

In the two years following our discovery, a large body of evidence suggested the zoonosis of these cancer and neuroimmune disease causing mouse viruses had occurred via biological therapies including vaccines. Especially vaccines against viruses. Scientists agreed it was possible that XMRV particles were present in virus stocks cultured in mice or mouse cells for vaccine production, and that the virus was transferred to the human population by vaccination.

In 'Plague of Corruption' we raise the broader question of the enormous risk of using animal tissue in research & the mixing of it with human tissue for the development of medical therapies while covering up value and efficacies of natural product therapies like cannabis, homeopathy, energy therapies and other medicinal plants.

Courtenay's book is important as the stories need to be documented before the censorship, fraud and corruption by the scientific journals reaches the level where all truth in science is replaced by propaganda replicated by the mass media as has happened over the past three decades.

In no area of medicine is that more apparent than vaccines where the complete failure of the vaccine program world-wide is clear, especially the failure of the measles, polio, chicken pox and HPV vaccines.

It is now clear that zoonosis of HIV in the 80s, SARS in 2002, MERS, Ebola in 2014, Zika in 2016 and now COVID-19 (Coronavirus) occurred not as in nature or as we have been told by health authorities but by nosocomial transmission.

That is by the xenotransplantation of animal blood and tissue via vaccines and a contaminated blood supply, resulting in the loss of tens of millions of lives and the explosion of chronic disease.

Dr Judy Mikovits

Preface

Thalidomide: The Artist Formerly Known As 'Distaval'

The following is taken from an advert carried in the BMJ British Medical Journal, dated 24th June 1961, Vol 1, No 5242, p12:

The large picture in the advert shows a tiny girl holding an open medicine jar, with the lid in her right hand... accompanied by:

"this child's life may depend on the safety of 'Distaval'. Consider the possible outcome in a case such as this - had the bottle contained a conventional barbiturate. Year by year, the barbiturates claim a mounting toll of childhood victims. Yet it is simple enough to prescribe a sedative and hypnotic which is both highly effective... and outstandingly safe. 'Distaval' (thalidomide) has been prescribed for over three years in this country, where the accidental poisonings rate is notoriously high: but there is no case on record in which even gross overdosage with 'Distaval' has had harmful results. Put your mind at rest. Depend on the safety of

'DISTAVAL'
 TRADE MARK

REFERENCES: Practitioner, 1959, 183, 37. J clin. exp. Psychopath., 1959, 20, 243. J Coll. gen. Pract., 1958, I, 398. Brit. med. J., 1959, 2, 635. Med. Wld. (Lond.), 1960, 93, 26. Brit. J. Pharmacol., 1960, 15, 111."

The Impact of Science on Society

Original edition 1953

by

Bertrand Russell

'Scientific societies are as yet in their infancy...

It is to be expected that advances in physiology and psychology will give governments much more control over individual mentality than they now have even in totalitarian countries. Fichte laid it down that education should aim at destroying free will, so that, after pupils have left school, they shall be incapable, throughout the rest of their lives, of thinking or acting otherwise than as their schoolmasters would have wished. But in his day this was an unattainable ideal: what he regarded as the best system in existence produced Karl Marx. In future such failures are not likely to occur where there is dictatorship. Diet, injections, and injunctions will combine, from a very early age, to produce the sort of character and the sort of beliefs that the authorities consider desirable, and any serious criticism of the powers that be will become psychologically impossible. Even if all are miserable, all will believe themselves happy, because the government will tell them that they are so.'

Table of contents

Warning and thanks (p.5)

Preface (p.19)

Table of contents (p.21)

Introduction (p.23)

Prologue (p.29)

1. Starting out in business (p.35)

2. Getting into bed with government (p.39)

3. Moving on and waking up (p.45)

4. Going deeper in to the mire (p.59)

5. Statins to start (p.69)

6. HPV vaccine carnage (p.87)

7. Catching on to cancer (p.105)

8. Follow the money (p.123)

9. Informed consent (p.143)

10. Considering Common Law (p.147)

11. Who is the criminal? (p.159)

12. Being well, eating well (p.175)

Postscript (p.189)

Appendix (p.191)

Introduction

In a time of universal deceit - telling the truth is a revolutionary act.
George Orwell

We all have our War Stories and mine are just as boring as those of the next man. Just like holiday snaps our stories paint a picture of places been, people seen and, along the way, some wake up calls. Epiphanies in posh speak. The book title comes from how it took 20 years to join the dots, of health and the law; but not the law as I'd been told and sold, and not just for 20 years but for the first 61 years of my life. It's identity shredding when you go from true to awful, from legal to lawful. Since 1997 I was slowly to discover that health is ensnared by a massive legal squid and together go hand in (rubber) glove.

This book has been 15 years in the making. Triggered, in major part, by a comment made over a dinner in Washington, DC. Tom Wheeler was a digital addiction master - best known nowadays as a 5G pusher - but back then he headed up the CTIA (Cellular Telecom and Internet Association). An 'ultimate' wheeler dealer is Tom. He continues to be a long-term political influencer, rainmaker and lobbyist. It was him who, in 2005, (vegan alert) over a juicy steak in DC said, "There's a book in you". He has always had friends in high places as, fast forward to 2013, President Obama appointed him the Chairman of The Federal Communications Commission.

Back in 2005 I was traipsing back and forwards from England to the US to help launch a business text messaging service; in total, I visited the US nearly 30 times in three years. It seemed apt that a boy from London was being schooled by a man in

DC, both being private City states. If only we'd had a Roman with us too, for the complete set of triumvirate - of those hidden states within Countries. But I knew little of that then.

Søren Kierkegaard was so on the money, "Life can only be understood backwards; but it must be lived forwards". Little did I realise back then, that my unhealthy obsession in 'health' and the law would evolve over the next 15 years. Peeling back layers of an onion, enough even to make my eyes water and, in 2019, enough to almost make a boy weep - following two arrests.

This is my timeline from birth to being 62 years young. Born as a 1957 model, by 1962 I was regularly gigging in the street, grazing knees, falling over, getting up, and eating worms as playtimes. Medicine and chunky monkeys were rationed back then and my Mum believed that Mother Nature hadn't stolen my healthy immune system from her latest son; her third, and final, screaming brat.

It wasn't sickness she worried about but medicine; 60 years on she still does. My Mum is 91 now and though mainly bed bound she still regularly recalls the horrors of the Thalidomide scandal. Her words spoken painfully, even now, as if she knew she'd dodged a cruel bullet for her boys. Mind you, the marvellous Distaval came with science and editorial credentials so, 'Put your mind at rest'. It was, "highly effective... and outstandingly safe".

Little did I realise back in 1957, as a chubby nought year old, that I was actually still-born - as in born dead - but no one let the Informant, my Dad, in on the act. You'll need some trust to read through to the end of the book but, if you follow the timeline, it should all make a bit more sense.

At 62 now I'm grateful to have gotten this far as, daily, I appreciate I'm about two thirds dead (with luck that is - and no banana skins).

Along the way, and suddenly, I've only recently realised that I'd been somewhat asleep for 98.5% of my 62 years. As in, much more woke from January 2019 initiated by a two week 'law' trip to Spain. I'd finally had some grit fire-hosed out of my eyes.

The last 15 years have passed in a heartbeat while I've moved steadily away from health as a business to Wellness as a lifestyle. Along the way I've met some truly remarkable health heretics and heroes - whose deep research, then changing beliefs, marked them out from the distracted herd. This is more their story than mine as I'm simply the scribe. If this book - my template - helps you, then my time won't have been wasted (and, at the time of writing, nor will your eight quid).

For nearly 50 years I've ridden motorbikes and, occasionally, defied the laws of physics too. If the world is spinning at 1,000 mph then why as a teenager couldn't I stay on a Honda 50 going at an extra 40mph (with a bent frame granted) that cost me all of five hard earned quid? Rutted fields and road tyres that's why my little, muddy, apprentice Neophyte. With such a fine motorcycling pedigree it was obvious that the Isle of Man, home of the famous TT road races, beckoned. Not wishing to embarrass Mike Hailwood and Giacomo Agostini I put off going there until 1991. We (that is judy - my wife - and I) slowly fell in love with the Island and moved there permanently in 2008.

In the noughties, while visiting the US so often, I thought I'd got used to their 'let's start a shiny new war with a country beginning with another letter of the Alphabet' mindset. Usually one that Americans can't pronounce nor find on a map - but can bomb, heavily, 'with deep cratered shock and awe' Mr Prez. Anyway, with Teflon Tone, 'our' homegrown War Criminal having a total deep throated bromance behind The

Bush, it was time for me, too, to ship out from Blighty - and this was my decade. Lady Di had already had her chips cashed out, and the writing was on my tunnel (vision) wall too.

Slow forward to 2020, as age comes to us all if we're lucky (and not in a Merc), we have now passed the period of Peak Health, while spending ever more to treat the sick and be sick. Seems you can talk about Merc car crashes (a bit) but Merck manufactured vaccine wreckage? Not at all; especially at polite dinner parties. Yet, with an 'upwards only health budget', US infant mortality ranks in 34th place in 1st year survivorship tables. The Country with the most childhood mandated vaccinations, coincidentally. That's despite spending twice as much as any other Country on 'health', also coincidentally.

Infant mortality is not just soiling its nappy, it is fully in the financial toilet too. The causes of all this 'health' slowly dawned on me from the late 1990's until today. It's as if their health spend makes them well, less: healthy. In a, le$$ is more, type of way. Why should we worry, if we're not American? Well, quite simply, because what starts out Stateside blows steadily to all corners of the world - and the climate of ill money is blowing at ever more parts of the world with more than a full frontal assault. No market - sorry, child - left behind and all that.

But medical change comes slowly.

Entrenched interests need to move on or retire - only then, it seems, can Status Quo Joe more easily permit himself to see with new eyes. If the funding of scientific investigation depends on serving the interests of the funder, then the ultimate cutting free to think is the death of people who had certain mental conditioning. As we progress we must remember that 'dead men tell no tales'. Little was I to realise how important that phrase would be as, in January 2019, I watched my Spanish lawyer friend, robed in black, be robbed of justice in plain sight. In court he literally died a 'black death' of injustice but my eyes back then couldn't quite see it. All a part of his job... of his sworn oath.

Yet, within days, my fork in the road had turned me into a full-blown 'legal' versus 'lawful' researcher. Within 12 months, and 1,000 hours of research, it was clear our 'birth' certificate confirms that we are all unwittingly still-born, in the birth certificate column. As in born dead and lost at sea - 'legally' too. Yes, that is really the biggest red pill to swallow my little Neo. The strawman and 'legal fiction name'; the elephant in the room, in black robes - his secret hidden in his trunk, with a hard to pick padlock, stamped BAR. Many are called to it but too few are chosen.

A while back, in England, the wise fellas at the top of the tree caught on when we stopped eating our own urine (topped off with a fresh dollop of faeces) served from easy access open sewers; then... our health improved. Go figure. If we stopped that delicious starter in our habitual thinking then, by adding in some decent food our teeth stopped dropping out too. Sanitation and nutritious food, the greatest inventions in health history - who'd have thought it? Almost the greatest 'invention of dis-covery' was the not so humble lime; a million sailors would die before we'd conquer scurvy. Who's the lemon now, my dear Horatio?

My personal stroll had started out full of optimism, all puppy dog and Mary Poppins. But now at a fair gallop the 'health' system seems to have morphed expensively into a Stalin, Pol Pot, and Hitler route march. Sounds a bit more than far-fetched granted but stick with me, and do bring a sick bucket. But with 'death by medical system' (the posh word is: iatrogenic) being the number three killer, after heart disease and cancer, we may need to redefine health and 'the Big Killers'. So, read on - while you fully observe the existing 'health' world and how it is currently defined.

Prologue

Three things cannot be long hidden: the sun, the moon, and the truth.
Siddhattha Gotama

This book will be read differently by everyone. The topics covered are wide ranging, merely reflecting a drop in the ocean of our body's complexity. They say we can't have one thought without having another and that putting things in context helps determine our own meaning. We can be sick in so many ways while we can increasingly access an 'expert' for each body part, each doing a deep dive into his or her narrow silo. But only in their chosen field, considering others as lesser secondary citizens. They research ever more, ever deeper but ever narrower - losing sight of the whole, the countless bodily interactions. There's little money in being a generalist. So, in studying ever more they think they're progressing. It's not just proctologists who like to keep their hand in.

But a fightback model is emerging just as we're seeing the dying thrashes of the 'body as meat' model, with whole body science arriving over the horizon. Clever meat-monger types might even dust off 'The Body Electric', by Robert Becker, from three decades ago. We're seeing the end of assumed 'surrogate end points' in clinical trials, of 'harms hiding' in short term trials, too. We need specifics that relate to one another; specifics that the real world actually... validates, repeatedly.

Those specifics are emerging in Functional Medicine, underpinned by the final re-recognition of 'food as medicine' and that Mother Nature might, indeed, know best. Your own unique: mind, body and spirit to be viewed as a whole, and how it does function best as a whole. Your unique, free at birth body; the ultimate gift from your Mother to be cherished, with luck, for a long and Well life. A long life, beyond just an un-animated meat sack. Filled with water.

The industry, for that's what the sickness medicine profession has become, is: scientifically corrupted, financially rewarded and politically controlled.

They are not my words, but typically those of Dr David Healy and Peter C. Gøtzsche, two internationally renowned researchers who have questioned the ethics of the medical industry. Prolifically cited in Medical Papers, their books, too, more than hint that all is not well. Dr Healy having written, 'Let Them Eat Prozac', and 'Pharmageddon'. Dr Gøtzsche wrote, 'Deadly Medicines and Organised Crime - how big pharma has corrupted healthcare'.

Meanwhile the patient is languishing as a cash cow on the side lines, with his trolley up on bricks or laid out comatose in a very expensive barn, ready to be milked. We all expected that the trusty regulators should have ridden over the hills to our rescue. But the more you look, and deep dive, the more you realise they have taken a deep sleep that even Rip Van Winkle would have said, was more than a bit long. That shocked me, too, gradually tweaking my brain over five sleep deprived years. But those years were not wasted; looking back they helped build a new mental model. Many have asked, "Why the obsession?". Why? Because mentally none of it made sense, if you weren't on mental 'health' med's.

Well, who'd have thought it Vicar? How did we end up here, fully right up the junction? The train I'm on gathered speed over time, yet it's not as if I didn't have the chance to jump off; but, actually, I chose not to. Or 'it' chose not to let me. Quite. While progress towards Wellness has to battle the black hole and financial clout of the 'health' industry, most people do actually prefer being Well; they've just lost the map. Many maps they do find are written by others, pointing away from

30

the end of the rainbow, and our treasure trove, within.

The '$ick industry' loves to infantilize their patient, the artist formerly known as people, via their, pure as the driven snow, profit centre motives. 'Let's resection your bowel guys, and while we're about it - your wallet too... and your kids' inheritance'. And before you know it, you're at the point you need to sell the seafront condo in the Maldives to pay for the heart med's and tool kit used on Grandpa. 'He's a great guy isn't he?'.

Along the way you'll find that disease-mongering really is an art form. That by simply going to the Doc' with a sprained ankle, a torn ligament or a swollen hand you may, before you know it, end up on the couch with a cuff monitor on, and a cholesterol test will be winging its way to the lab. Followed by a quick catch-up on multiple vaccines for the holiday and for their winter season (but not in the future spent in the Maldives).

In going in unwittingly as a person and coming out as a patient, you should take a conscious lesson from a famous Spaniard who said, "I went to sleep a painter and woke up Picasso". But, over-specialism in medicine now has them painting by body parts and by number.

The coffee I like filtered but not my media. The scripts from five media billionaires, those 'Silicon Valley filters', are handed out locally as news. It's scripted synchronicity at its best. Your data is their gold. For they guard your toll bridge every hour via: FaceTube, Twatter, or WasteBook feeds. It seems the digital divide thermostat is set to Fahrenheit 451 (hot enough) to burn the dangerous books. Pinterest were at it, too, by blocking 'anti-vaxxer' search results in February 2019.

In early March 2019 the film 'Vaxxed' was deplatformed from Amazon Prime availability, yet the free thinkers had their day as, on Sunday 26th January 2020 'Vaxxed II' was shown in London. YeeHaa! Let's cheer for a 2020 Vision. So, the patient remains ill-informed and that's how the pHARMa industry likes it: infantilized and uneducated about medical harms. Hearing the pros and cons is all we ask; yet, currently, the con$ are 'winning'.

Their forward plan being spelt out in broad daylight in Agenda 21 and Agenda 2030 if we note the narrative. There is always an agenda. You do know that don't you?

Truth, though, is begging to escape - everywhere; even on modern British television.

Jordan Peterson first came to my attention in his interview with Oxford educated, Cathy Newman on Channel 4 television. I say interview cautiously, as throughout she was on transmit and little receive, as a fire-breathing feminazi journo. The chainsaw and napalm would come out later as the script unfolded. Likely, to ensure that Jordan never got up from the mud wrestling canvas. Only he did, with true honour - while she was going for a slam dunk knockout, in or outside the ring, with what seemed like a below the belt approach. He was goaded, but gossamer winged, replying with light as a feather evidence. If the death of Buddy Holly was the day that music died, then 16th January 2018 was the day when: identity politics and compelled speech bit the dust too. Finally.

However, in reading his book 'The 12 Rules for Life', I was caught up short at page 37. His words fairly exploded from the page, 'Before the Twin Towers fell - that was order. Chaos manifested itself afterward. Everyone felt it. The very air became uncertain. What exactly was it that fell? Wrong question. What exactly remained standing? That was the issue at hand..'.

But my question is different from that posed by Jordan; why

focus on the Twin Towers only? That three buildings collapsed on that infamous day has clearly passed him by. He missed Building 7. It too collapsed on 11th September 2001, in real time, on the same complex beside the 'twin' towers. As if demolished, yet fully on film; actually in: reel time. But not for prime-time showing. Not, that is, promoted at all by The Biased Bropaganda Corporation. Luckily, drum and camera roll, the BBC's Jane Standley was recorded stating, "The 47-story Solomon Brothers',(i.e. WTC-Building 7) situated very close to the World Trade Center, has also just collapsed". Guessing luckily, it turned out, roughly 23 minutes BEFORE it actually did so. Yet, fully pulverised to dust specks - no desk, nor phone, nor chair remained intact. No steel frames either. We can see 'The Sun' headlines now, 'Not only did Freddie Starr eat my hamster but Fred Dibnah fessed up about the Triple Towers and Twin Planes'.

Six years on, up fired Richard Porter on Tuesday 27th February 2007 saying the BBC no longer has the tapes of that fateful day due to, "more cock-up than conspiracy"... Yeah right, Dickie! Richard is listed as the Controller of English at BBC Global News. More like a compelled speech controller.

So, I will market my books through 'Building 7 Publishing', to tip a mighty remembrance to the innocent murdered by their own US government that day, and to those killed and maimed since.

Jordan says in Rule 8 of the 12: 'Tell the truth - or, at least, don't lie'. Takes some beating. So, might he focus on researching a 13th Rule for Life - "How not to demonise a billion Muslims nor force them behind the bush". In plane sight. Time for us all to move past the distraction of Gemini the Twins, and rise up in honest enquiry around the: Three Fates. Nearly 20 years on from that - inside job - day.

It is a tall order, I know.

As our final curtain closes, in chasing the daylight, we likely only have strength to say a few words with our last breath. Apparently, we usually include: 'I love you', 'I'm sorry' and 'I wish'. The impact of those last two words can be lessened if we repeat this little ode:

There'll be two dates on your tombstone,
And all your friends will see 'em,
But all that's gonna matter,
Is that little dash between 'em.

courtenay-adam-lawrence :heading

Isle of Man

20/02/2020

1. Starting out in business

The purpose of a business is to create a customer.
Peter Drucker

In 1975, after completing a year at an engineering college, I started work as an engineering apprentice. I joined a local authority for the opportunity to train in six different departments, each for three months; the idea being within 18 months I'd have a diverse taster of skills. Well that was the intention as confirmed in the job advert. However, being bright and after 17 months in the same department I'd sussed, with Einstein like research ability, that the management of Tunbridge Wells Borough Council wasn't exactly Kaizen based. In addition, the project assignments I was given were too formulaic and too locked down for my creative bent.

It was my first observance of governmental sloth. Easier to walk through treacle. Up close and impersonal with the energy vampires. Some of the 'workers' were told to slow down so as not to 'show up' their colleagues. Many was the day, I thought, 'have I got another 40 years of this purgatory?'. Well, no, I decided I hadn't.

I then joined an engineering consultancy in West Sussex having chanced upon a role as a civil engineering draughtsman, which I really liked. From there it was three years as a freelance draughtsman which I loved even more, as it entailed regular change. I was meeting new people, working long hours, Saturdays too, and buying my first house. Some days I would commute two hours each way to Hammersmith and when that was too wasteful, I rented a flat in West London - paid for by lashings of overtime.

It was a London era before Hugh Grant had rocked up, and you could rent a mansion for tuppence three farthings a decade. Obviously, the plunge pool was boarded over since Mick Jagger had put a Roller in it but the excitement of London still lingered. Those long hours and hard work just kept expanding; however, I was younger then and all Duracell puppy dog. On speed.

By 1983 I was a quarter century into living and decided that being a recruitment agent was the way to go. The role needed sales skills, a trader mentality and an ability to form trusted relationships. Suddenly Bromley, in Kent, was the sexy place to be and I was dipping my toe, teeth and tongue into something new and fast paced. I'd take desk lunches and judy, as ever, was packing me up with a veritable feast of goodies; in the days where pudding with every meal was in vogue. Fortunately, all my nervous and physical energies kept the chunky monkey demons at bay.

By 1985 I was 27 and it was time to leap out of the comfort plane of paid employment. Without a parachute. For my first decade of work I showed up and in return someone deposited numbers in my bank account at the end of each month. Some days I would even work hard. But 27 was the age when boyhood heroes die; especially Jim Morrison and the great Jarno Saarinen - so I needed to get my skates on.

I would form my own company and engineering recruitment was to be my initial vehicle. I'd had 18 months working for others in recruitment and now it was time to fledge the nest. The business was all built on networking and relationships. In short, it was exciting. Plus there was no clocking in and out which had so irked me, as an apprentice, a decade before. My beloved Uncle John exemplified the 'back me or sack me' philosophy - and he didn't have a boss either, come to think of it. Buccaneer memories last for some.

In January 1985 I rented an office in London, and my business partner was set to join me four or five months later when I'd got things up and running. I was always at the front end of the production and this, my very own pantomime horse, was no different. He was a back office man, well structured and less emotional. We were a successful team. In time we'd supply engineers all over England and graduated to having 140 engineers on contract. More than anything it was fun, and when the hours were really long I'd sleep in the office. Within three years we also had an office in Grimsby (oh, the glamour) supplying the booming Humber bank area with contract staff.

The big break for us came in 1988 when we also landed a supply contract with CASA (Spanish Aerospace) for design and prototyping staff. Spain was part of the Airbus consortium; a plane made in several bits and glued together in France. As it was made of cutting edge carbon fibre, that's not too flippant. We hired a Spanish lawyer and we were off to races - sun, sea, sangria and tapas. That started my decades long love affair with all things Spanish, and my deep dive into learning the language and culture.

It also showed me how the world really worked - behind the curtain - at a governmental and tax level. The Spanish do many things well, but having lots of carbon fibre expertise hidden under a Bullfighter's cape was not one of them. Our role was to be middlemen, sourcing the best talent worldwide to work in Getafe, south of Madrid. Carbon fibre was new in the aviation arena and there were only half a dozen countries who had the requisite talent to ensure the wings (or engines) didn't fall off a plane. Well, rarely anyway.

The contract and culture was only part of the issue; the big elephant in the money trunk was tax - or lack of it. It was agreed with UK tax officials that we could set up a Jersey company to pay 80% of the salary to the contractors (body shoppers in old money) and pay the rest as a local per diem. A legal tax-free wheeze no less, resulting in gins all round at

Pimm's O'clock. On the Santiago sun deck.

Soon our cars got an upgrade. First a Ford Fiesta 'on the firm', then an Escort Turbo - a la Harry Enfield's Loads-a-Money - followed by a bells and whistles BMW 325i with leather seats, electric sunroof and a lumpy car phone unit in the boot. We used to dream of mobile phones and a septic tank at the bottom of our garden. "You were lucky", said my Yorkshire pal.

Finally as the 1980's ended, in August 1990, I maxxed out on an Audi UR Quattro (the original rally supercar) and 30 years on it still lurks in the garage with a mere 183,000 miles on the digital dash. The only car I've had fully airborne, with turbo on max boost, to which my fully relaxed Wife gently chided, "Hark dearest, is it a little short of the ideal to be attaining such lofty progress, though that is in no way to question your clearly exquisite driving skills?".

But I may have misheard how an 'F' or two may also have punctuated the airwaves.

2. Getting into bed with government

I believe that all government is evil,
and that trying to improve it is largely a waste of time.
H. L. Mencken

In 2000 I was a chemo fan; well, not a fan but an unbelievable ignorant fool - please form an orderly queue to punch me in the mouth, but only once as it was a bespoke... chemo'therapy'. So in 2001, there I was investing in a University spin-out company called Oncoprobe... A friend of ours having died recently convinced me that I was to medicine what the Beatles were to song writing. But in reality I was to cancer treatment what George Bush was to peace.

Between 2004-2007, while travelling regularly to the US, I saw an even madder country coming into view and that was Britain (my home Island then) - but not for much longer. They say, 'he who looks on sees most' and from afar I could see Tone, the War Criminal, bestriding the world grinning ever more Cheshire cat like, knee deep in his transatlantic Bushy Bromance. One in need of a severe pruning.

In those 30 Stateside trips I encountered many sayings that just plain baffled me. The Brits and the Americans are two nations separated by a common language someone once said, or maybe more than just once. One saying I'd heard was, "Are you blowing smoke?". On closer inspection it seems that phrase has real roots. Blowing smoke actually derives from a quaint 18th Century medical practice of having smoke blown up your back passage... rectum - "Well it didn't do the patient much good, Nurse". The objects needed (by Dr I. Smoke, FRCS) gave no hint at all of quackery and included: a nozzle, a fumigator and a bellows. Plus, of course, 8 ounces of Old Holborn Rough Shag. And pursed lips bestriding an anal trumpet with stamped instructions to 'blow only', in 194 languages. Hot air? Definitely not, look it up on Wikipedia.

As the new earner - sorry, science - of climate change came into view in 2010, the world was stocking up on magical, costly lightbulbs that took four years to warm up and emitted less light - sorry, CO_2 - than something Thomas Edison would have been ashamed of a century before. Apparently, a normal bulb in my bedroom, if I can locate it, emits more light and heat than The Sun. That constant temperature Sky ball (that few ever ask about), might that have an effect, Granddad?

Anyway, clean tech was all the rage a decade ago. As a co-founder of a micro-turbine company, I was suddenly cool, sexy and hip (but not yet woke, clearly). Well, to be honest, not quite but the 'clean' technology could be spun that way. I was invited to attend the regular Manx Aerospace Cluster meetings, and a key task was to estimate future market demand and especially jobs. That way we wouldn't be caught out in short pants, in the planning and training department.

I recall one meeting especially clearly. The boys from BAE (British Aerospace) were on the Isle of Man and gave polished presentations on Sopwith Camel production and, if I recall, even more modern variants of warfare. One such was the Eurofighter Typhoon, a delta wing aircraft designed to deliver shock and awe to the latest alphabet enemy over cornflakes and (vegan) milk. The kindly details matter, I'm told.

One other (minor) detail that matters, was when the BAE Johnny highlighted the increasing Typhoon production during his presentation. It had the date on it and for clarity it said: '2023 War With China'.

You could have heard a pin drop but no one said anything. I sat there thinking I've just heard the forward planning of a war crime but, at least, the production engineers can predict when they can buy their Wives a new frock AND have two weeks in Camber Sands, in August. Chairing that particular meeting, at Tynwald Mills, was Martyn Perkins of Manx Engineers. Who said nothing either. That Martyn is now a member of the Manx parliament is interesting. Thank goodness we have green credentials and two pints of (vegan) milk.

The location was just as memorable for me as, fast forward nine years to 5th July 2019, it was to be the location of my arrest for speaking out about worldwide HPV vaccine injuries - and as a cause of cancer. I don't know which will be the bigger crime - it just needs time I guess. Best follow the money, parliamentary 'privilege' and enforced silence.

I actually spent five years between 2012 and 2016 working as a consultant to the Isle of Man Government. The role was as their Healthcare Innovation Consultant. Initially I worked in the Department of Economic Development (DED) as the role was primarily about new, high-tech jobs on the Island. Latterly I worked in the Cabinet Office alongside Policy and Reform Minister, John Shimmin. He had also originally headed up DED, and in both departments he made my role enjoyable and, more importantly, very satisfying. Despite long hours I loved it.

This was in spite of the fact that I also had to associate with a number of energy vampires. Quite simply, I realised that slow trudging through ponderous, treacle-like sludge was not for me. But I did learn a new saying: 'Never do today what you can put off 'til the next parliament'. I learnt that governments only tell half the story, omitting anything that undermined the clean tech impression. Tail pipe emissions were the total focus; along the way and simply ignored were power stations, coal, wood, lorries, energy losses, cost efficiency, and not very long-life batteries made of rare (and polluting metals). That sort of cherry picking killed my creative energy.

Fortunately I'd exited stage left, before, the Greta good trooped up and 45 years old men in suits started listening to a tearful 16 years old actress. Green religion is a story that dare not speak its name; that of cognitive dissonance. But, at least, Goddess Greta was Time Person of the Year in 2019, following on from such luminaries as Adolf Hitler (in 1938) and Joseph Stalin (in 1939 AND 1942). Perhaps, if we'd paid these gentlemen more money then their forthcoming skirmish would have been much colder.

With each year that passed it dawned on me that the patient discussion was happening less and less. It was as if the only thing that mattered was an upwards only revenue model. Nevertheless, I was meeting some world experts looking for a new place to beach their 'whale of an idea' technology.

Some were truly cutting edge, looking for a fleet-of-foot location to get rapid traction so they would not burn a whole load of cash (while waiting for bureaucratic decisions). At the time we even had an Ethics Committee, and hand-holding entrepreneurs to complete the paperwork was all part of the role. Innovators are not always known for compliance to processes; however, with clear signposts and regular nagging many did.

To try out new ideas and promote 'ManxBioMed' we held state sponsored bio-medical-ism events in 2013, 2014, and 2015. The first year was all about attracting 100 delegates - 99 represented failure, while 101 delegates was pure success. Hitting treble figures in the first week of December, to an Island in the Irish Sea, was no easy task. But if you have a Sally Carpenter as an organising shipmate 'fear not young Luke'.

There were four main reasons for relocators considering the Island: 1) lifestyle / reduced stress; 2) lower taxes, as the Island is an offshore jurisdiction; 3) faster legislative decision making; 4) a dash for cash, hoping wealthy Islanders would back their innovation.

The Island certainly is a lovely place to live and work in balance amongst Mother Nature. It still offers lower taxes, particularly by not starting expensive wars. We're more than ready, though, to squabble amongst ourselves. However, in terms of legislation, we can only propose secondary legislation - on bended knee to the UK Crown - as primary legislation is controlled through London. Think Bigger Brother and a tag along little 'un pulling at his shirt tails. For all that, a number of Companies have settled here but only a tiny fraction of those who looked us up and down. They had many reasons for not settling.

To oil the commercial wheels the Manx government put together an Innovation Fund of £10 million per year to assist start-ups. Impressively, it was to be £50 million over five years; although, sadly, it was to become pretty much stillborn. After just two years it had invested only a tiny fraction of the fund and the new jobs increase was woeful. Our Plan was not as good as we thought; in fact, we didn't really have one. Did I?

I travelled regularly to Universities to meet spin-out companies in: Oxford, Cambridge, Heriot Watt, Imperial College, Reading, Keele, Liverpool, Salford, Bangor, Manchester, Queens' University Belfast, and the Karolinska Institute in Denmark. I was meeting world-class researchers, all with a focus on an aspect of the human world; or on spinning out a company to 'save the world'.

Often, though, the experts seemed stuck in wheel spinning mode. They were experts because as (Nobel Peace Prize winner) Nicholas Butler said, "An expert is one who knows more and more about less and less". More than a few just wanted to be full-time, forever, researchers; however, they dared not admit that true commercialisation was the last thing on their mind. That way their idea could always be about to happen, not really real nor judged in truth. They were infected with reductionism as a species. And silo science.

My honeymoon period was over, as the model seemed increasingly broken - although not at the cash machine.

3. Moving on and waking up

It is simply no longer possible to believe much of the clinical research that is published, or to rely on the judgment of trusted physicians or authoritative medical guidelines. I take no pleasure in this conclusion, which I reached slowly and reluctantly over my two decades as an editor of The New England Journal of Medicine.
Dr Marcia Angell

Public Health might get 2% of the funding but chronic (not acute / nor accident) gets almost all of the budget. Once the bulbous Good Ship HMS Chronic Disease has set sail, very little can have her alter course.

I was spending hours per day on research - weekends and evenings too. It sure beat telly. Often, too, sleep was for wimps; fool that I was.

The range of health ideas I encountered in those five years I worked as Healthcare Innovation Consultant for the Isle of Man Government included: hearing improvement software, tumour tracing, light probe cancer screening, digital pill bottles, amalgam fillings (scandal) cover up, peanut anaphylaxis from vaccines, mushrooms to treat cancer, small molecule cancer therapy, ligand manufacturers, regulatory affairs, pharmacovigilance, tobacco plant to manufacture an alternative to breast cancer drugs, stem cell therapy, mental health games and screening, addiction, natural botanicals (mental health: mushrooms / medicinal cannabis), raspberry therapies out of China... , de-prescribing of drugs, women's health, diabetes, data devices, stents, human tissue, radiological screening, bed monitoring data devices, plastic surgery, stem cell biology, prosthetics, prostate cancer, digital infection monitoring, natural tooth regrowth, synthetic biology, blood testing, laboratory analysis of toxins in vaccines, recombinant proteins, cluster headaches, immunotherapy, robotic hernia repair, CAR-T therapies, breast screening, aspartame toxicity, glyphosate build-up, vaccine harms (of: flu, polio, MMR, HPV, tetanus, smallpox), bowel cancer screening apps, calorie counting apps, Omega 3 manufacture, early diagnosis of multiple system atrophy, cervical cancer pessary, cholesterol shenanigans, infertility therapies, implant harms (vaginal mesh / shoulder replacement), and, lastly, GcMAF cancer therapy.

The GcMAF cancer issue was throwback to a request in 2015, by then Chief Minister, Allan Bell, to meet David Noakes. Mr Noakes was pioneering a natural, less harsh, cancer treatment alternative to chemo 'therapy'. There is an ongoing saga around GcMAF... one, that will likely be included in a future book.

There are many forks in the road and one date where I decided to fork off, forever, from government was Thursday 16th June 2016.

At an 8.30am meeting with some high-up in health I asked, "Can I publicly debate vaccines, statins and anti-depressants with you?". The reply floored me, "We wouldn't allow that". Not the refusal but the 'we' part. It sounded oh so Common Purpose, so creeping Common Market diktat. A mantra of sick perpetuation, of couch potato and too many carbs.

So by 2017 I had fully detached from government.

A strange focus started to come along, not stress but a plan and purpose was coming into view. Working from home was - and still is - an increasing boon with no commuting and I get to sit in my dressing gown (and underpants) for hours on end. Most days the bra can wait, as can shaving.

But the best bit is three cups of morning coffee with full milk (and cream) and local honey. It's more addictive, by far, than crack cocaine. In short, a heaven of a sanctuary to relax and work.

Most importantly, with no commuting I get more time for thinking and in 2016/2017 that was all about improving local health. The Bee Gees sang, 'How can you mend a broken heart?' but my nagging ache of a focus was, 'how can I mend a broken medical system?'.

Gradually I sounded out all my contacts and started writing a weekly blog which forced me to do ever more research. I loved the 'work' but felt I was spinning my wheels. Meanwhile judy was ever the patient and loving home supporter. She didn't even kick my butt as there was no money coming in.

Steadily I was tripping headlong into medical negligence and that, of course, meant lawyers or, to some, ambulance chasers. I'd always known a few, chancing across them at local Executive Club dinners and numerous lounge lizard events. One thing I noticed was they seemed to miraculously have more homes than me, more holidays, more business 'interests' and fewer street 'l'argot accents. Their Wives had posher frocks too.

I was heavily into the research phase and I didn't just love it, I adored it. Amazon could hardly ship the books quick enough and with a water-cooled PC, I was on every Youtube site going - some of them even made sense. You could compare and contrast medical knowledge (fancy term for smelling b/s) in ways unknown to previous generations. The internet was paying for itself and some.

Increasingly, so much of it looked - well, how can we say this? - played not exactly with a straight bat, Vicar. In short - utter bollocks! And in even shorter shrift, a bit of a killing machine.

Hmm, I didn't come into this to be an observer. Increasingly I wanted to participate and rattle the gates 24/7. To be, in poncy speak, a change agent. Paid or unpaid. But I forgot to fully tell judy.

With a voracious appetite for new learning I was in my element.

Regulatory and capture were not words I'd heard mentioned together until Dr David Healy visited the Isle of Man in May 2017. David was, at the time, Professor of Psychiatry at Bangor University, and the author of 'Let Them Eat Prozac' and 'Pharmageddon'. Books in which he holds the feet of Big pHARMa to the fire. He has done likewise, in US law courts, particularly with the insanity of anti-depressant harms in causing normally sane people to carry out mass shootings. When you actually look at the evidence and medical history Stateside, from Columbine onwards, there's been decades of it and, of course, with less than zero press coverage of causes. If we follow the funding, of Bad Press and Big Pharma, we'll know why - causes harm effective cures.

I'd long been a fan of David's 2006 US FDA (Food and Drug Administration) shredding testimony, as still seen, surprisingly, on Youtube. He highlights mass collusion (and jail for some) over manipulated drug 'trials'. His video confirms how many punches you can land in just three minutes as a master orator. His evidence is a masterclass of a pummelling, of which even Mike Tyson would have been proud.

So, in May 2017 I'd invited David to speak about hidden and abandoned clinical trials. That topic wouldn't normally be aired by any on message health organisation, but knowing a lunchtime event organiser you can bypass 'official blocks' in Noble's Hospital.

Recorded over 90 minutes, David highlights Study 329, where

48

the FDA saw and scrutinised, submissions listed as Appendix A-G. Then, a loose tongued individual asked, "What about Appendix H?" - as in, where is it? When Appendix H was finally collected, it seems that the headmaster had already heavily marked it. In that a mere 77,000 pages of science was heavily redacted. Softer words than 'criminally hidden' but, to me, a black mark nonetheless.

That crime was further heightened when someone off guardedly asked, "So what is emotional lability?", but only after 20 of the great and good experts had signed off the trial 'science'. It appears that emotional lability is actually suicide and that - on a clinical trial showing drug harms causes - must never see the light of day. Hence, free black marker pens all round.

A deathly hush for patients and, yes, to me the FDA does = Fake Drugs Allowed.

We now have the current era of three and four letter acronyms wielding enormous medical power, with NICE in the UK pulling the clinical 'excellence' strings. WHO says? Not always the end patient that's for sure; their voice is drowned out by the NHS, CDC, EMA, HHS and MHRA. Then come the lawyers providing some extra medical muscle: the DoJ, The CIA, FBI, NSA and the UK's Border Force.

Let's now take a deeper dive on both sides of the Pond:

The General Medical Council is the ruling body for UK doctors. You need to be licenced to 'practice' medicine. If you have need to question a fellow GMC registered medic you can use the GMC Code 68; they then have a duty to respond, as your peer. But it rarely ever happens and if they do actually start the process, they generally back off. Or are told to. It's sort of old school, a gentle kick in the nuts while using a feathery quill blunt pen.

The GMC had a key role in slapping down - hard - on the biggest challenge to the vaccine model in the last two decades. That being: 'vaccines cause autism'. More fully, the MMR vaccine as the major cause of autism that for 20 years just won't go away.

From the late 1990's and Dr Andrew Wakefield, right up to 2018 (a year when Samoan toddlers died immediately after their MMR vaccine), and to the 2019 Corvelva lab test that can't find the rubella antigen in the MMR vaccine, but plenty else. Dr Wakefield had only asked if gut harms from the vaccine might be connected with the later autism diagnosis. One also where single vaccines based on science, not cheapness, were actually safer, and also a protocol that eliminated regressive autism.

Those who follow the GMC shenanigans would also come to examine the dark shadow cast over Dr Waney Squier - a world leading pathologist - who changed her view over 'shaken baby syndrome'. She too, was hung out to dry by the GMC in a vicious trial for questioning the real causes.

We should note that Sweden has totally reviewed their 'shaken baby science'. In Los Angeles, too, it is the number one cause of wrongful imprisonment.

But the GMC remain wedded to an outdated 'shaken baby hypothesis' as a total religion. A religion too big to question, because of where that might lead for unexpected sudden child deaths; of their often close time proximity to increasing vaccine schedules.

Maybe the GMC is really a Grand Medical Collusion entity. The GMC is, in reality, a colluding clearing house; a revolving door which goes from Pharma to Government and back again. And again. Shush.

CDC - The Centres for Disease Control is, as the name suggests, the body with a remit to reduce diseases across the United States. The CDC tells pregnant women that it is very safe for them to get a flu shot during any trimester. Meanwhile, in the published peer-reviewed literature, the CDC's own researchers have reported finding a sevenfold higher risk of miscarriage for women receiving a flu shot who'd also had a flu shot in the prior year. But 700% is neither here nor there in modern maths. Is it? The Patient Information Leaflet even states, 'there are no studies that have been undertaken on the safety of this practice'. Note: practice, not reality.

They will rue the day, when they ignorantly claimed in 2012 that, 'vaccines do not cause autism'. A generation betrayed, as autism has gone from 1 in 10,000 in the 1980's to 1 in 30, today in America. But other countries are catching up.

The above should be read in conjunction with watching the film, 'Vaxxed'. It features, Dr William Thompson, a scientist at the CDC. In Vaxxed he confirms the decade long cover up of regressive autism - after MMR vaccination - that African American boys had a 3.4x greater risk. There was a particularly heightened risk if children received the MMR vaccine before 36 months of age - the earlier, the more severe autism symptoms.

Dr Thompson even has 10,000 documents as evidence to widely share, if called upon. In 2004, he was asked to shred them but with a sense of duty and scientific integrity he didn't. He has supplied his research papers to Senator William Posey and Congressman Dan Burton. In August 2014 Dr William Thompson stated, "I regret that my co-authors and I omitted statistically relevant information in our 2004 article published in the journal 'Pediatrics'". In Vaxxed Dr Thompson said, "oh my god I cannot believe we did what we did, but we did, it's all there". If made public it would be the biggest medical story of the decade.

Also in Vaxxed, one paediatrician said, "I feel I've been lied to, they wanted to look at the data, but there is data they chose to ignore. It is a big deal for a physician but for the fact for the last 10 years we've been destroying the brains of patients. It's been based on a lie and a cover up".

The Head of the CDC during the noughties was Julie Gerberding, who would receive her own reward upon leaving that post - a highly paid job with Merck from 2009. The very same Merck over whom, while at the CDC, she used to have major 'oversight'. She must have taken a leaf out of the book of the British philosopher, Ashleigh Brilliant, who said, "I either want less corruption, or more chance to participate in it". Door and revolving spring to mind.

The CDC has form as a 'wrong un', as from 1932 until 1972 they carried out the Tuskegee Experiment which involved deliberately injecting African Americans with syphilis, and then leaving them to die without treatment. Effective penicillin treatment was withheld by the CDC so that the 'experiment' could continue.

Finally, after a six year battle to stop the 'clinical trial', whistleblower Peter Buxtun highlighted the atrocities to the world. He played a key role in the Congressional Hearings that followed, and attended the Tuskegee memorial centre opening in 1999. Truth eventually sees the light of day but it can take six decades. The majority will eventually learn also that, yes: the MMR vaccine causes autism - but it is taking a while.

DoJ - Department of Justice - Dr Andrew Zimmerman is a paediatric neurologist and a former Vaccine Court Expert Witness who, in June 2007, swore an affidavit that vaccines can cause autism. He was immediately fired by the DoJ. Finally the deposition by Dr Zimmerman in 2017, nailed what would be his legacy, that vaccines do cause autism. The originally called Robert Zimmerman (better known as Bob Dylan) sang, "for the times they are a changin" should have added... eventually.

Del Bigtree highlights in Vaxxed that when the DoJ (Department of Justice) requested the files, Dr Thompson heard that his colleague Dr Coleen Boyle had brought in a lawyer. So, we had Government scientists suddenly lawyering up on a children's safety study. Over MMR and autism.

HHS - The US Health and Human Services have long sought to keep the findings of the Hannah Poling autism compensation case secret - the evidence of the MMR vaccine causing autism being 'legally sealed' from view.

Vaccines have been declared in court as being, 'unavoidably unsafe', while the HHS acts as the pharmaceutical Co's lawyers.

But the role of HHS in marijuana / medicinal cannabis is far more in view. "I am not a number I am a name" as proclaimed in 'The Prisoner', beloved of nostalgia buffs of 1960's British TV. Well, might the prisoner be called to respond to number: 6,630,507? Likely not, as the US Government has claimed it - it being a Patent number they hold on cannabis plant compounds. The 1936 film: 'Reefer Madness' highlighted cannabis 'harms' as the official narrative.

FDA - Food and Drug Administration - In 2010 a (US) False Claims Act was filed by virologist Stephen Krahling, and Joan Wlochowski accusing their employer, Merck, of falsifying its mumps vaccine test in claiming an effectiveness of 95%. Their accusation centred on the abandonment of full disclosure, 'gold standard' testing, by mixing animal antibodies to human samples, in order to falsely indicate increased human antibodies. The FDA knew of this 'procedure'. However the human antibodies on their own, would never protect against wild mumps, in those inconvenient but real world situations. These 'special' tests showed complete efficacy but only against the mumps vaccine virus. Some call it scientific fraud.

Problems abound and not just with vaccine integrity.

Dr David Healy shows further FDA 'regulatory capture' on Youtube highlighting the inability of the FDA to see raw, unbiased trial data. In a scorching three minute video he laments their woeful lack of scrutiny. He highlights the suicidal acts in registration of three new mental health drugs. Quoting from it, "an MHRA article that includes three placebo suicides that weren't on placebo in clinical trials. People who a week later, after going on Prozac, went on to suicide. The FDA publicly declared an increased risk, but 'we can get this risk to go away' if we control for age and sex. This suggests that the clinical trials were invalid to begin with".

He highlights the jailing of researchers for entering fake data in this programme. Fake or bogus patients do all sorts of interesting things: they get better and they don't suicide - it's just inconvenient for the audit trail if they do.

The FDA really have been at it for some while; 'it' of course being: cover up. This from volume 49, No 107, of the Federal Register on 1st June 1984, 'although the continued availability of the (oral polio) vaccine may not be in immediate jeopardy, any possible doubts, whether or not well founded, about the safety of the vaccine cannot be allowed to exist in view of the need to assure that the vaccine will continue to be used to the maximum extent consistent with the nation's public health objectives'.

MHRA - The Medicines and Healthcare Products Regulatory Agency is the designated competent body that enforces and administers medical device law in the UK. It holds enforcement and regulatory powers to ensure the safety and quality of medical devices.

Back in 2011 the PiP breast implant scandal had yet to be fully in the public eye. But behind the scenes the MHRA was firmly in the spotlight, thanks to the work of Brian Toft, Professor of Patient Safety at the University of Coventry. His concern was of the fitness for purpose of the CE marking process - the necessary stamp of approval for medical devices. It had been acknowledged for years that there were not just gaps but severe failings in the genuine regulation of medical devices, including: replacement hips, implantable defibrillators, heart valves, and breast implants.

NIH - The National Institutes of Health (US). Dr Bernadine Healy was the former director of the National Institutes of Health. Speaking with Sharyl Attkisson in 2008 she initially thought that the vaccine autism link was, "just silly, on first superficial reading". But Dr Healy said, "the more you delve into it, if you look at the basic science, what I came away with is the question has not been answered. We have to look to see if there are children, whether of metabolic or genetic makeup, that makes them more susceptible to vaccines, plural, or to one vaccine in particular. We have the tools today that we didn't have ten years ago. Maybe we would find vaccines should be spread out a little longer. I think the public would respect that. I think the Government has been too quick to dismiss the concerns of these families without studying the population that get sick. I haven't seen major studies". Dr Healy, we applaud you. More so as the NIH later confirmed that it receives significant royalties from licencing HPV vaccine ingredients to Merck.

NHS - The National Health Service is that beloved UK institution, that none dare criticise. However, former MP, Andy Burnham used his last speech in Parliament in 2017 to question NHS failings. He called for, "a criminal investigation of a wholesale cover up, on an industrial basis, of tainted blood within the NHS going back decades". He said he couldn't "live with himself" if he did not use his last parliamentary speech in that way, as it is estimated that it concerns 2,400 deaths.

Mr Burnham, highlighted the extent of this negligence on 25th April 2017, saying, "when we have these documents of American warnings in 1975, of derived blood products taken off convicts, on skid row. Some seven years later, the Oxford Haemophilia Centre in 1982, sent a letter to all UK centre directors to just crack on, to send out blood products. This was despite knowing that initial production batches which were injected into chimpanzees, to test infectivity, can't guarantee quality assurance for all future batches. That is the proof in my view of very serious negligence, from pooled blood by using (NHS and other) patients as guinea pigs. By administering these concentrates into patients requiring treatments, who have not been previously exposed to large pool concentrates… Then consider that a Health Minister's Papers are comprehensively destroyed, under something they called the 10 year rule. I've been a Minister, I've never heard of a 10 year rule, have you Deputy Madam Speaker? It's a new one on me. A Ministers' papers destroyed, without his consent".

Really NICE - in 2014 the UK Parliamentary Commons Health Select Committee investigated conflicts of interest of NICE (National Institute of Clinical Excellence) panel members, one where 8 out of 12 panellists recommending the lowering of statins 'risk' score had direct financial ties to the statins manufacturing industry. Numerous accusations from independent cardiologists and GPs is that the current appointment process to the NICE panel is not transparent nor fit for purpose. First, statins were given to those with a 30% 'risk' of heart attack, then to those with a 20% 'risk', then to those deemed a 10% 'risk'. Meanwhile, we should note that decades long worldwide studies confirm that all cause mortality goes up as cholesterol goes down. Ooops.

EMA - The EMA (European Medicines Agency) remit is to ensure that medicines across Europe are safe and effective. No problem there, if it worked. Formerly based in London, now for purely political (trigger alert) Brexit reasons, it has been moved to The Netherlands. Yet, even the cosy European Parliament had enough back in 2011 as they refused to sign off the EMA accounts. They felt the EMA was too close and cosy to the pharmaceutical industry. Their vote, when refusing to sign off the accounts, was passed by 637 votes to 4 - hardly the narrowest of margins. A bit like a Germany versus England penalty shoot-out in football.

The European Parliament also ordered a special investigation into the EMA's source of funding - the majority of which comes from the very industry that it regulates. Coincidentally. What very few know is that the EMA exerts a python like strangulation on anyone, forever (and a day) who wishes to discuss EMA 'business'. As usual.

"Time gentlemen please!", was a regular refrain in pubs when I was growing up. A friendly call for 'last orders at the bar'. MEP's meanwhile, are a less hurried bunch of drinkers, as urgency and a closing of the cash register is not normally in their business model. Let's ask Mr Blobby, about a slimming pill called Mediator (aka benfluorex) which caught MEP's attention. It was withdrawn from the market slowly. How do we define 'slowly'? Well, here, it was 10 years after notification of harms. The EMA refused to release the 'clinical' trials data for three years, claiming that to do so, "would undermine commercial interests". It's business as usual.

But the ultimate accolade for Regulatory Capture is the go anywhere UN whose hidden presence reaches everywhere, even to provision of commercial code numbers for the little towns of Bride and Andreas, on the Isle of Man - but not (yet) for Santon. Even the Jurby runway is UN ready...

4. Going deeper in to the mire

The media dresses things up. There's a lot of inaccuracy.
Chuck Berry

Is someone pulling my ding-a-ling?

Come the 2nd July 2017 in celebration of turning 60 years old, and with nowt falling off, I had a glorious picnic with judy, by the river (deep and Mountain high, Tina?) in sunny Glen Auldyn. A stunning blue skied day and not a chemtrail to be seen. California (or Australia now) must be getting our share, I mused.

In the evening, a meal was kindly laid on not by me but by a restaurant owner - and lawyer too, as it happens. We were speaking softly to each other, then. Half of those present were lawyers and, even better, I didn't get a bill, in pounds nor guineas - from anyone. I'm glad I was sat down - though the blue touch paper was well alight. Over hors d'oeuvres the chats morphed into legal cases. For easy starters we chatted about statins, then went full fat into the low hanging fruit of medical implants before the cheese and biscuits. Then we peered into the worldwide vaginal mesh horrors, to confirm that nothing was off the table. It was evident these lawyer chappies can spot an angle, perhaps with implants - a bent one, if breast implants out of France were to be any guide.

I ventured forth with some deep dive of my Wellness nonsense, such as "One med is two med's too many". The fuse wasn't just lit by now, a bonfire of the sanities was fully underway. One lawyer chimed in, defensively stating she'd, "die if she didn't take her med's". It was as if I'd slept with her sister, her Mum AND her favourite cat. I masticated on her medicated state and shut the heck up. If judy had been there

I'd still be suffering the after effects of an Ice Age stare. Now, even I thought, was not the time to bring up the boring statistic that 'death by doctor' was ranked as the number 3 (or number 1 depending on who you read) cause in the US. So let's split the difference and call it a silver medal position as she was European. Cheer$ my dear doctor! Or should that be Che€rs?

The human body isn't a machine, each cell breathes. Each individual is a living breathing organism, created to its unique genetic blueprint which then interacts with its environment in complex ways. Carbohydrates, fats and proteins aren't fuel, they're energy carriers. Seems that there are two 'Fuels': ATP (adenosine triphosphate) and Ketones. We're built to be hybrids that can run off both of these fuels (trigger alert) a bit like a car that can run on diesel and petrol at the same time. But not a (petrol) Suzuki 1100 Powerscreen on the M1 late at night, when all your Wife wants to do is get home. Anyway, humans having trans-itioned into being bi-fueled to make the grade.

But, and it's a biggish butt, many people have become reliant to run only on ATP and get most of that ATP from one energy carrier, in the form of carbohydrates. We make ATP from carbohydrates, fats or protein in tiny little energy factories called mitochondria that we have in pretty much every cell in our bodies, especially in muscle cells.

If we stop eating carbohydrates and have allowed our fat burning machinery to become dormant, we can burn protein to produce ATP. That system is there only for emergencies because the main protein energy carrier in our bodies is muscle - and who wants to burn their muscles, Mr weak and skinny? To get good at fat burning we need to restrict carbohydrates and fast - as in 'go without' - to help our gut work better, and to work out better too.

There's a bonus too. Ketones are our brains' favourite fuel - preferring ketones even to glucose. You might have come across people who've been working hard all day saying they forgot to eat but their mind stayed crystal clear. That's often because they've been relying on ketones.

We've identified so far that the engines of our cars have got messed up, because of the way so many of us live. That's why focusing on putting slightly less fuel in the tank, as health authorities are suggesting, simply doesn't work. People just fill up more often. We need to focus on what's wrong with our engines. When we've fixed our engines, we can easily shift our metabolism into a state of nutritional ketosis whenever we need. We will have become what we call metabolically flexible and it's at that point we earn our badge saying that we are 'keto-adapted' and ready to party!

There's been a lot of science and clinical studies to work out the best things we can do to fix our engines to become keto-adapted. It doesn't involve taking any drugs or diet pills, but being a complex problem in which our internal signalling systems (that control both our feeding behaviour and our energy metabolism) have got mucked up. We have to do more than just one thing. No, there isn't and never will be a magic pill.

No one size fits all. Just like clothing. Don't go hungry but do fast, and adapt steadily. For me certainly, low carb high fat is the way to go. With a 'better' diet you will move more readily, and steadily de-stress. With your brain being a cholesterol organ, that's a no brainer. Isn't it doctor?

For such a high fat to finish, in endurance events, it's a big ask of Big Government, just as it was previously with Big Tobacco who called, and paid for, the shots.

In August 2018, a film escaped out of the EU surprisingly, that bastion of big corporate business interests. Any film with a title of: 'Big Food and Big Pharma Killing for Profit' wakes us up, especially as it features Sir Richard Thompson, former Physician to the Queen, who is withering in his attacks on the sick industry. Rumour has it the Queen came off statins in 2006 but I couldn't possibly comment. Although, she is looking well these days and, likely, it's not just the five aside footie in the Palace rose gardens.

Increasingly the language of 'health' has started to change. It's been up-regulated while a growing challenge of DGR (Doctors Gone Rogue) is now coming from within the higher medical establishment - not just from the rankers and filers. Some traditional insiders suspect a bit of table rigging is taking place and that the level playing field has likely lost its 'spirit' level.

One such insider in the film is prominent Cardiologist, Dr Aseem Malhotra. He's a clear communicator in raising more than an eyebrow or two while, as the author of 'The Pioppi Diet', lowering the heart rate. Maybe, though, being an acclaimed Cardiologist he's raising the blood pressure of his less enlightened colleagues. Handing our health to us on our plate. The real answer is, in reality, in our hands not theirs.

Professor Thompson and Dr Malhotra both raise concerns about the mass medication harms of statins due to repeated, simplistic and financially driven 'score' lowering of otherwise well patients.

It's late February 2018 and I'm in Thessaloniki, Greece for a medical conference on vaccines. Yesterday, I viewed the White Tower in the town centre, as impressive a six hundred year old building as you'll ever see. The White Tower I'd assumed was named after purity of intent although, as it's a former military fort, that may be a romantic jump too far. The name actually came from when it was painted white, as in it being 'whitewashed'.

While in Greece my email in-box started to fill up, interestingly with the same theme, coincidentally - a near identical message about, sadly, the UK's current 'lack' of antidepressants. The friends who had emailed me all sport a different stripe, so I received articles from their 'news' channel - their newspaper of choice: The Times, The Telegraph, then The Independent.

Soon my in-box could take no more but it had piqued my interest. So I went a huntin' and found that, yes, The Daily Mail, The Daily Express, The Sun, The Times, and The Irish Times, ALL had articles on 21st or 22nd February 2018 'coincidentally' explaining that a neat and dandy extra 1 million (or more) people 'should' be on antidepressants. You'd think they had all been handed, a lazy, pHARMa script.

A nice round number is a million people but then, so too, is nought, zero, nada! Reading such consistent 'investigative and unbia$ed pieces of journalism would make anyone depressed - well, not quite everyone if we may, just for a second, play the cynic.

Let's see if these 'lone wolf' and hungry journos arrived at their unique scoops, fully independent of each other.

So, as an unpaid guesser, without a union card but armed with a water cooled search engine I went looking for similar topics in The Guardian. I was in luck! It too was coincidentally leading the charge with: 'It's official, not only are antidepressants not snake oil nor a conspiracy - they work'. That's all right then, if we could first define 'work', which seems an inconvenient and little probed, four letter word. But IF we examine what the word 'guardian' means, it's: 'someone to look out for us, someone who serves our best interests, someone to look up to'. Someone, no doubt, not given to spouting the collective view$ of other$, hand fed to them as a signed off, pre-prepared, pre-approved, 'independent' mantra.

Daily Mail - Return to Sender - Their Health Reporter had been busy too, as on 21st February 2018, stated that millions (plural) more of us should be taking antidepressants citing claims that they do work, and that GPs should be 'dishing' them out. The researchers had 'warned' that only one in six people were receiving effective treatments for depression with 10% of British adults now on antidepressants.

However, if a week is a long time in Politics then, hats off, it seems 48 hours is even longer in journalistic terms. By 23rd February we were 'treated' to this about-turn headline: 'Doctors say 'hyped' antidepressant study is misleading patients by ignoring the dangers and side effects'.

It quoted Professor David Healy, former Professor of Psychiatry at Bangor University (author of 'Let Them Eat Prozac') saying the benefits were hyped while the harms were hidden. He also criticised the short term (eight weeks) duration of the studies. How dare he? Professor Healy continued, "You could put alcohol through these trials and show it is an antidepressant - but it wouldn't be a good idea to have 10 per cent of the population taking alcohol". How dare he, times two? This is the same Dr Healy who found time to research and write the book 'Pharmageddon'.

Bush Telegraph - Send Me a Missile - Penned by the Health Editor no less, the Daily Telegraph stated that 'at least' a million more Brits should be on anti-depressants, citing Oxford University (doff caps, you plebs at the back) led research with findings published in The Lancet, no less. Cited too were over 500 trials featuring 21 'med's' over four decades. The Telegraph lamented that GPs were often 'squeamish' about offering 'medication' for depression. It did, however, 'warn' that the best known antidepressants, such as Prozac and the most widely prescribed, Citalopram, were found to be among the least effective...

64

For The Times they are a Changin' - In The Times, too, their Health Editor took it up front and centre with: 'More people should get pills to beat depression, millions (plural again) of sufferers would benefit, doctors told'. Plus a snazzy Prozac piccie. Not just The Times but in The Irish Times too - to be sure, to be sure - with coincidental headlines: 'Antidepressants work for treating depression, study finds'; following up with the debate denying: 'New analysis puts to bed the controversy surrounding medication, says professor'. So it seems even that great wordsmith, Bob Dylan, had it all wrong; but, then, 'for The Times they are a similar' wouldn't likely have topped the charts.

Simply Expressing a View - The Daily Express, like a bullet train, was on narrow tracks and very on message, jumping its green signal, not waiting for the stop light with its headline: 'Antidepressants DO work and millions more should be on them' it chimed in. But, could the message be from the selective steam age, leading more well-intentioned drivers to sadly chuff about, while powered by masses of industry funded hot air?

The Independent View - The Patient 'Voice' - About time the patient voice was heard. One lady aired her struggles with mental illness for 17 years and had tried most pills available. Her view was that antidepressants absolutely worked for her, "antidepressants can enable a person to participate in their own life, when they simply cannot otherwise". The Independent also aired a counterpoint of view in the same article: "I was like a numb zombie on antidepressants - pills should only be one part of the solution. No other treatment paths had been suggested to me and it was only after I had gained two stone in weight, without changing my diet, and was throwing up a few times a week that I realised that maybe my antidepressants weren't working for me".

Ask An Insider? - Seems we're not learning from even recent

history as, in October 2016, Business Insider stated, 'In every single Country the OECD looked at, antidepressant use was on the rise: in Germany it had risen by 46% in four years'. Normally those pesky Germans win soccer matches on penalties but it seems, that this time, they may concede late goals - but of a different kind. Spain and Portugal struggled to keep up but made double digit 'advances' in antidepressant prescriptions. Iceland 'led the pack' with one in ten people now taking an antidepressant. Hooray.

Storm Clouds Block Out Even The Strongest Sun - The Sun was in on the act too, coincidentally, in strict 'no tabloid, and no pill, left behind' fashion. It had antidepressants as a main story, encouraging its readers to 'Take More Happy Pills'. If Freddy Starr had eaten your hamster, you'd sure need them. That may not take us too far forward in a reasoned debate but ever greater pill use is confirming storm clouds are gathering that will forever block out the sun, and not just in Liverpool.

Back on 13th May 2015 there was a report in The Mirror on the findings of Dr Peter Gøtzsche, a Danish Medical Researcher (and co-founder of the Nordic Cochrane Centre). He investigated antidepressant deaths and claimed that across the US and EU there were over 500,000 deaths, in people over 65, per year. His view is that such psychotropic drugs should almost exclusively be used in acute, short term, situations. He feels their long-term use is immensely harmful and their use requires, for many patients, a firm plan to 'taper' off their use over time.

Perhaps that's why, this time, The Mirror wasn't invited to the 21st and 22nd February 2018 Fleet Street Party? Or perhaps they just chose not to go? Peter also found time to author: 'Deadly Medicines and Organised Crime'.

Mad In America - With apologies for reaching beyond British shores - it's not just the chill of US pHARMa weather that finds its way onto British shores given time. One day all countries will have to go 'upstream' to treat causes not just demand cures; but the money doesn't lie there. Talking of following the money, it was amazing that the FT (Financial Times) didn't lead on upselling antidepressant use; after all, with such a monetary message prize, cynics might have assumed they would - bowler hats off to your independence, guys and girls!

Robert Whittaker, is a journalist and author of, 'Mad In America', and 'Anatomy of an Epidemic'. His presentation to a British Parliamentary Committee was entitled: 'Causation Not Just Correlation - Antidepressants Increase The Risk of long-term Disability'. He studied people on US Government Disability funding due to Affective Disorders. His studies, over 25 years from1988 to 2013 found that in 1994 there were 440,000 people on antidepressants, while in 2013 there were over 2,000,000 on antidepressants. The Percentage of the population who used antidepressants (in the past month) was constant at around 2% between 1988 and 1994, but it had risen to around 9% in 2012. That's a near 500% increase on both measures - we should investigate that increase and its upstream causes.

Zoloft, also known as 'Sertraline' is an SSRI (Selective Serotonin Reuptake Inhibitor). If compared with a treatment of Zoloft plus exercise, and also exercise alone (i.e. without Zoloft), it was found that with just exercise alone, at the end of ten months, there was a 70% reduction in people still suffering with depression.

In the real world, then, exercise seems to win and doesn't generally incapacitate people. For many, but not for all, exercise is a kinder and cheaper, long-term option.

So, if the shoe fits, hold the front pages of Runners World. The new model of mental Wellness and kinder support beckons. With exercise and healthier foods as a newer, cheaper and gentler 'prescription'. One that is more compassionate than current offerings, but will fill less, lazy (and paid for) column inches of British tabloids and broadsheets.

5. Statins to start

You can die of the cure before you die of the illness.
Michael Landon

In May 2018 I tucked into a big healthy dollop of a book, 'Healthy Eating: The BIG Mistake'. Sometimes you read a book that wakes you up with more than just a Usain Bolt out of the starting blocks. You literally get a physical jolt too. That the book was diligently researched by Dr Verner Wheelock is clear. I suddenly realised how much I had missed; how I'd been so distracted by the medical industry.

The book supported other insights from 'The Cholesterol Con' (the book penned by Scots GP, Dr Malcolm Kendrick). Please both, take a bow for confirming: all cause mortality goes up, as cholesterol goes down. In any case, the subtitle of Verner's book should have kicked me out of my slumbers, it being: 'How modern medicine has got it wrong about diabetes, cholesterol, cancer, Alzheimer's and obesity'. That sounds like a big enough gig for anyone in one lifetime - by the use of sound science to boot.

Clearly Dr Wheelock has taken a (partial) leaf out of the musings of Dale Carnegie, whose follow-up would likely be: 'How To Win Friends and Alienate People'. Those people, of course, being 'experts' in the perpetual 'sick treatment', med's to the max, business. The same people financially wedded to the '$ickness is health' mantra - but maybe unlikely to get married in pure virginal white.

By page 70, he is quoting the BMJ regarding cholesterol lowering interventions, "any reduction in deaths from heart disease was counterbalanced by deaths due to other causes and there was no effect on ACM (All Cause Mortality)". Those who are fixated solely on heart issues need to study major harms often triggered by statins, including: cancers, cataracts and, if the fairer sex is reading this too, female suicides. You do know that don't you? Dr Beatrice Golomb clearly does, and has the studies and published, independent, peer reviewed Papers to support the real world evidence.

World leading Cardiovascular Surgeon, Professor Sherif Sultan of the Galway Clinic has presented a razor sharp 35 minute video. He doesn't hold back and won't be gagged, serving up scientific evidence in abundance. He's more qualified than most to comment, with a veritable roll call of scientific and medical excellence: Professor of Vascular and Endovascular Surgery, President of the International Society for Vascular Surgery, as well as Chairman of the Western Vascular Institute.

Speaking at a Functional Medicine Conference, the title of Professor Sultan's Youtube lecture would draw in anyone: 'The Known Unknowns'. If it had been entitled 'the unknown unknowns' then I would have been expecting Donald Rumsfeld to turn up with a fair dose of shock and awe. I wasn't disappointed, as the Professor's presentation contained just that, with confirmation of: scientific fraud, hidden cancers, regulatory collusion, commercial cover up and a deliberate, long-term, burial of countless bodies of evidence.

Criminal is the word for the statinisation of otherwise healthy people - as clearly seen by those who take any time at all to do any independent research.

Professor Sultan opens with, "I was the Surgeon who was about to be gagged by certain organisations... that was five years ago, I'm still standing and things are changing very rapidly". Clearly we needed to hang on to our hats as Professor Sultan continued, "Today, I hope to change everything that you have learned about statins over the past 50 - 60 years". If we weren't listening properly he continued, "It's very clear that we have major problems with the regulators".

He cites countless trials and some 36,000 published articles for which the authors have received industry funding while defrauding the whole medical service and, worst of all, the hapless patient. The video also drew from the films '$tatin Nation and Statin Nation II'. Dr Beatrice Golomb, who has investigated induced suicides due to statin prescription, added, "In its effect it's scientific fraud... it's organised crime".

TIME to Confess - 53 years of CHOLESTEROL lies.

1961: Time magazine front cover: Ancel Keys - Father of the lipid hypothesis.
1984: Time magazine front cover: The War on Fat and Cholesterol goes Global
2014: Time magazine front cover: Eat Butter (finally acknowledging they got it wrong).

It took Time Magazine 53 years to confirm their CHOLESTEROL mistake, which was based on a worldwide deception by scientists and medics.

More than a deception, it is also a conspiracy of silence by the Regulators and their financially motivated, industry insider, Committees - and GPs too.

Professor Sultan continued, "Ancel Keys was the guy who created the havoc. In 1969 Eisenhower died, they all met up, and as the President was a loved man what was to 'blame'? they asked. Was it sugar? Was it tobacco? Was it fat? Tobacco - the Big Lobby they couldn't go against. Sugar - the Big Slob they couldn't go against. So, who was the poor guy? It was fat" - with a small but soon to be big,'F'. The word FAT was very soon to be demonised; to be more than a four letter word. It was a manufactured food fear; they demonised the humble egg too (as healthy a food as you can get).

71

Seeing $tatins through a $40 billion / year telescope - To quote the video, "We are observing the revealing of the utmost medical tragedy of all time. Never before in history has the medical institution deliberately produced a life-threatening nutrient deficiency in millions of otherwise healthy people. Any negative studies are discouraged and critical researchers are blackmailed".

The Problem is not Cholesterol - likely it's the drugs - Lipitor, Crestor and Zocor significantly increase the risk of new onset diabetes mellitus by four fold, and is irreversible and renders current diabetes mellitus uncontrollable. One in three women will develop diabetes mellitus if they use statins, regardless of their age. Erectile dysfunction is 10x more prevalent amongst statin taking young men. Yet, when statins are discontinued over 50% had a full recovery. Still it's TRAGIC, utterly tragic.

As if that's not enough, by taking a statin there is a significantly increased risk of colorectal, lung and bladder cancers, plus muscle atrophy and mind impairment. Statin use increases the likelihood of stroke and brain haemorrhage too. By avoiding statin use you GAIN two years of life. BUT Pfizer eliminated these findings from their clinical trials. Statin use actually increased the level of calcified plaque in the arteries, as evidenced in real world 'trials'. If that isn't scientific fraud and criminal deception, what is?

In the film '$tatin Nation', Cardiologist Dr Peter Lansjoen confirms, "Cholesterol is essential for life and a little higher cholesterol is associated with longevity, decreased malignancies and improved defence against infections".

Also from the same film, Dr Katherine Farady developed five new illnesses in one year while on Lipitor, a statin.

At least in 2017, finally, the FDA (Food and Drug Administration) increased the risk warnings on the statin drug labels.

But, continued Professor Sultan, "We are facing a major cover-up story".

Hardly NICE is it? - A group of eminent medical experts wrote a warning letter on statins harms to the Chairman of the NICE (National Institute of Clinical Excellence) highlighting their concerns over the: medicalisation of healthy individuals, hidden true levels of adverse events, hidden data, industry bias, loss of professional confidence, and conflicts of interest. Yet, the 'safe' cholesterol level continues to be lowered - flying in the face of ALL the evidence - while 'disease-mongering' millions more healthy patients via their currently trusted Physician relationships. Based on no reduction in long-term trends of heart disease. The cholesterol number is lowered by 14 men in a dark room, where 9 of them are paid by the statins industry.

Professor Sultan was really getting into his stride now, with the all-important statins method of action, the smoking gun of evidence... The epidemic of heart failure & atherosclerosis that plague the modern world is aggravated by the use of statins.

A statin is contra-indicated for: patients over 62 years of age, any woman, and all children. As I'm 62 I paid attention but, as I haven't lost my mind just yet, I've avoided statins like the plague and still do. The evidence of statins harms is everywhere.

Also, on Youtube, Professor Sultan gives vent in a four minute 'quickie' video highlighting statin use as the cause of erectile dysfunction - it's not hard is it? No, sadly Linda, it isn't. Many say a more natural 'statin' is red yeast rice and increased intake of niacin - a dietary regulator of cholesterol - along with vitamin C to provide elasticity in the arterial wall.

Might K9, be less a wonder drug, and more a dog of a drug? - Of course, there's always a new wonder kid, a billion dollar blockbuster, on the block. So sexy it sounds like a car, the - wait for it - almost James Bondesque: PCSK9 Inhibitors. This is the latest attempt to (sad and mad?) block cholesterol - the substance that's in every human cell; our last line of defence against a nutritionally poor diet, a lack of exercise, a puff of smoking, along with a time loaded gun of chronic inflammation. Expect the short-term clinical trials to be front page wonderful; the long-term harms to never see the light of day, and the mouse model 'evidence' to be buried young, and selectively.

Fat Chance That Cholesterol Is (Actually) To Blame.

Interesting studies have come out of Norway. It seems that the real world evidence, over decades, IS that low cholesterol kills you earlier. So statinistas, put that in your pipe and smoke it; or maybe not. Dr Malcolm Kendrick, author of 'The Great Cholesterol Con', confirms that men and women with LOW cholesterol have INCREASED mortality risk.

The HUNT2 Study mirrors what they also found in Austria, over decades, too. Ooops! Another inconvenient truth. Dr Kendrick's own remedy is to tuck into haggis, him being a proud Scotsman.

Perhaps next we'll hear that the Moon, after all, IS made of cheese and if it is we should all tuck in - but only if it's high in natural fats, of course. So essential to health is it, that cholesterol is found in every one of our cells.

I would have referred you to Dr Kendricks' Wiki page but, as of February 2019 it was removed; him being deplatformed for speaking out against this multi £/$ billion scam.

Stateside, academic Dr Beatrice Golomb has focused her

research on the balance of statin treatment risks v benefits, a context that gives meaning to those opposing statin views - the yin and yang of real life. Dr Golomb has studied female physiology as particularly affecting violent mood swings and has studied suicide ideation for both sexes too. Hardly 'cuddly kitten Blofeld' but there you go.

A statins trial recently featured in a British daily paper. The trial followed more than 5,000 male patients over a twenty year period. But whoa! Or should that be 'wo' as there were no (repeat, no) WOmen on the trial - men only. Maybe WOmen were in short supply in the Rolodex of trial commissioners; but having 50% of the patient group fully excluded strikes one as, well, a bit skewed since you ask. That's more of a coin flip with only heads predicted to land, face up, each time. Good odds - or maybe even, odd goods?

But any debate should cover Number Needed to Treat (NNT) for effectiveness and focus on the 'drug gateway' aspect of statins - a drug which, once prescribed, leads on to the patient needing another drug, then another. Or maybe the odd hip and knee replacement is on the cards when cholesterol is driven kicking and screaming from the body.

The Good Doctor Kendrick supports increased patient autonomy and careful med's de-prescribing for better whole body health. But first, we have to break free of mass medication, a driver of so many addictive 'medical' substances. Maybe we are too casually listening to that 1960's Eagles classic, Hotel California, "You can check out any time you like, but you can never leave!".

More cholesterol is needed as we age - the long-term, country wide Japanese prefecture studies confirm: with low cholesterol we die earlier. But, then, with the Japanese not being Big Pharma captured, they're not fans of upselling medical interventions. At the younger age scale, they stopped their schoolgirl HPV vaccine trials prematurely, seven years ago. Evidencing serious, real world harms, their lawyers are at least making some money, even if Big Pharma will be footing some serious bills.

With my background of having been the Healthcare Innovation Consultant for 5 years to the Isle of Man Government, and through my research into health and Wellness, I was honoured to be invited to address the Isle of Man 'Social Affairs Policy Review Committee' on the topic of statins.

The following Hansard transcript has been reduced in length for topic focus, but not altered.

SOCIAL AFFAIRS POLICY REVIEW COMMITTEE Statins
HANSARD
Douglas, Friday, 7th December 2018, PP2018/0189 SAPRC-S, No. 1/2018-19

All published Official Reports can be found on the Tynwald website:
www.tynwald.org.im/business/hansard

Published by the Office of the Clerk of Tynwald, Legislative Buildings, Finch Road, Douglas, Isle of Man, IM1 3PW. © High Court of Tynwald, 2018

Chairman: Mr D C Cretney MLC, Ms J M Edge MHK, Mr M J Perkins MHK
Clerk: Mr J D C King, Assistant Clerk: Mr B Awkal

Statins

The Committee sat in public at 3.13 p.m. in the Legislative Council Chamber, Legislative Buildings, Douglas - Social Affairs Policy Review Committee, a Standing Committee of Tynwald.

I am David Cretney MLC and I chair the Committee. With me are Mr Martyn Perkins MHK and Ms Julie Edge MHK. Today we welcome Mr Courtenay Heading who will be giving evidence on the topic of statins.

Q1. The Chairman: would you like to make any opening statement?

Mr Heading: If you want background I will give that later on, but I am quite happy just to say I think statins are one of those great scientific and medical frauds perpetrated for 50 years based on scientific collusion, regulatory capture and driven commercial interests that do not understand the majesty and the interconnectedness of the human body.

Q2. The Chairman: Have you seen the Department of Health and Social Care's Chief Executive's letter of 23rd November and do you have any comment on it?

Mr Heading: I have seen it. No comment.

Q3. The Chairman: Okay. Did you finish the Parish Walk this year?

Mr Heading: Seven in a row. No blisters because I ignored medical advice and listened to my friend who is here today. So, yes, 85 miles, no blisters; 173,000 steps.

Q4. The Chairman: Absolutely.
We are a tiny population; why should practitioners in the Isle of Man go against the United Kingdom best practice?

Mr Heading: If best practice is short-term studies and leaving out the original study, which is Ancel Keys back in the 1950s ... He looked at 23 countries but ignored the 16 that did not fit with his cholesterol hypothesis. So scientific fraud from the 1950s and TIME magazine highlights this; it took them 50 years, until 2014, to say we got it wrong on cholesterol. The world gets it wrong slowly. So it is science not democracy; it is truth not in the majority.

Q6. The Chairman: Tell us more about your efforts to engage health professionals in debate.

Mr Heading: It has pretty much come to nowt. I believe it is an institutional problem, not an individual problem. They do not want Wellness; there is no money in it. It is a repeated medical model throughout the world that is driven by huge interest, huge inertia and does not understand Wellness. So when I come up with different debates they get churned out at the very highest level, all the way down the system. People tell you stuff silently so they will tell you they support your view but they will not come to a public, filmed debate. So that is quite evident. It has been difficult but Wellness Wednesdays, I will do them free, anywhere, but it will not be in a health building. The mantra is continuation treatment, not causes and not upstream, and it is quite debilitating but what else are we going to do?

Q7. Mr Perkins: Would you liken your stance on statins to a bit like the smoking revelations back in the 1950s?

Mr Heading: In 1954, a mouse - just the first - was coated with tobacco tar and it was about 40 years, 1994, before that proved to cause cancer from smoking. In 1994 I think the CEOs of the major tobacco companies said, 'It is neither addictive nor causes cancer,' and I think a few years after that there was a $207 billion fine on that industry. I may have got the figures wrong but I think I am broadly right. Absolute collusion, denial, short-term trials, drugs that you are not meant to take for life. It is the same with smoking as it is with statins. They are unbelievably harmful to at least 85%, maybe 90%, of people and they are not intended to be taken long term. So they left out the countries, they did a short-term trial. We need more cholesterol; it is a disrupter of your mitochondrial function, so both your battery of life and your cancer preventing human system and as cholesterol goes down all-cause mortality goes up. We can no longer put this in a silo. Cholesterol has never been shown to cause heart disease. A shock to most people. They need to do their homework.

So that started a journey. But I did learn a lot. I learnt a lot about scientific collusion, I learnt about universities doing clinical trials without ethics approval and it was absolutely criminal what I saw and it just made me pretty mad. So I thought I will help health. I became a health care adviser to the Isle of Man Government, to work at home, dog at your feet, cup of nice coffee - and by coming and bringing 60-odd companies, hosting 60 companies to the Isle of Man, I wanted to improve health. But then I realised slowly, painfully that none of them really wanted health, they wanted diagnostics, drugs, devices, perpetuation, but not upstream causes.

So in that I gradually lost faith with many of them and realised that debate was not going to happen with anyone that is inside the tent, because those who got us into this mess will not lead us out. We have to have different debates and we have to work collaboratively with doctors who have been sold a medical model, which is drugs and multiple interactions, but no three or more drugs have ever been trialled in medical combination. So that journey of seeing lunacy, madness, insanity, putting friends of mine on 10 drugs until they commit suicide, takes you to a very different place. We must not continue this; we must de-prescribe, we must understand that food is medicine. We must understand that this Island could be a sacred space and lead the world in telling the truth, with no legal protection on oath in a parliament or somewhere similar.

Q9. The Chairman: We heard your non-comment about the Chief Executive's letter. Have you engaged at any time with the Director of Public Health, whose responsibility is some of the matters you have just described?

Mr Heading: Even less no comment. (The Chairman: Okay.) Not only perhaps would somebody - let's not make this personal - not attend my debates - the last one cost me £6,000, that happened this week, so it is a tough gig - not only will they not attend, perhaps they may even have said last December, 'None of my team will attend either.' I left a near isle because I will not have compelled speech and identity politics.

Q10. The Chairman: Okay. Is there anything you think we should be recommending specifically to Tynwald?

Mr Heading: The current health review will fail. It is £270 million worth of perpetuation spend. I have said this in front of 11 witnesses to Sir Jonathan Michael and the secretary, Clair Barks. I have emailed Chris Robertshaw and been to his home, and been to the home of the Chief Minister. It is not as if I am unknown. I am not always the most temperate, but these things I believe in many cases, not too strongly, are crimes against humanity. So the policy will not change whilst those doing it are handle-turning perpetual motion. We have to define Wellness and we have to say this Island is one of the fittest on earth. I defy anyone to turn up here with a cycling team, a walking team, a swimming team, a young kids' outward bound team. So I think use parliament but say let's have an open debate with medics in a space where we can say, 'Do they really need to have a patient on seven to 10 meds? Is it really right that a protocol can condemn people to death when you put eight or 10 drugs in combination with each other?' It is insanity. So the policy will not work. Define Wellness. It is very different. We need to stop even going anywhere near that and have this honest debate - I go back to it - this sacred space. But we are not getting that with the health review. It has got a very tight remit and they think we should have an upwards only spend.

Q11. The Clerk: May I come back to a question which the Chairman asked earlier? As drafted it said why should practitioners in the Isle of Man go against UK best practice? I think you said because what we are referring to as UK best practice is actually bad practice in your view. (Mr Heading: Yes.)

Mr Heading: ...
But the best practice has been regulatory captured. If doctors really analysed how much the cholesterol level has been lowered over the years, how they have disease mongered millions, and particularly women who need more cholesterol as they age ...

Q13. The Clerk: Can you tell us a bit more about the smoking example, which I think you talked about a decision in 1994, or was that a court case? Where was that?

Mr Heading: I can be more accurate in my dates if you give me a little time to come back to you.

That is certainly a 40-year, maybe even a 50-year, mass collusion and the science was in, they knew in the 1950s that smoking causes lung cancer, and they hid it and they used enormous lobbying power, the likes of which only the current pharmaceutical industry has probably twice as much power. So I think we have got a golden opportunity to recognise the body, but only if we tell the truth. Glyphosate has now 10,000 people suing the company. It will bankrupt it. One case, 20 years of denial. It is always the same template: the people who are in the business of keeping you perpetuated, perhaps weakened - in 20 or 30 years they have to die or retire or have moved on.

Q15. Ms Edge: I would just like to ask really, if I suddenly become well and want to be one of these people that is coming off statins, what are the consequences of withdrawal from statins?

Mr Heading: They are Hotel California drugs. You can check out any time you like, but you can never leave. It is that process when you ask a lady how her husband is and in the street she tells you he has committed suicide - he has started on the ultimate gateway drug, a statin. I was not prepared for that, and even when we went to a barrister with huge amounts of research for the 10 medicines he ended up on, that process completely failed him by medical treatment because the medics do not know how to get them off. It interrupts your body in up to 100 ways. The liver has 300 active pathways; the body is unbelievably complex and we come along with a chemical, and it has only become a chemical so that a drugs company can patent it. The natural botanicals, the natural world we have around this Island is fantastic: unpolluted; there are not heavy chemicals, and we have lost that. We think the only treatment or the only training a medic should have is about four and a half to five years at medical school and about half a day on nutrition. I would love to do the world's first walk … anyone on a statin or a drug against me - first one to 100 miles. I will do it undrugged, I will provide the air ambulance.

Q16. Ms Edge: I have never been prescribed statins but I am not sure, do you know when you are prescribed them are you given a leaflet with any of the side effects and about withdrawing or stopping them, because some people choose to if they have some side effects?

Mr Heading: I am not a medic and give no medical advice. But they should. If we were educated, culturally with informed consent … We do not have informed consent here. We break, I think, the Montgomery ruling every day. We may even break the Nuremberg Code on Medical Experiments. We certainly break human rights law. I love this country but there comes a time, as Martin Luther King said, when silence is betrayal. So I do not know what they do. I do know they will disease monger you and lower the level, through private committees in London and some of them could have 14 members of whom nine will be from the cholesterol industry. These are hundred billion dollar drugs. They do alter your mind. If we read Lipitor Thief of Memory by Duane Graveline; if we read The Cholesterol Con by British GP Malcolm Kendrick; if we read The Pioppi Diet by Dr Aseem Malhotra; if we watch the 35-minute video masterclass by Sherif Sultan. They risk everything to stand out and they say it. The science does not add up. We have a deep natured sugary diet and then we take a statin into your body and that debilitates you in ways you do not even know; it is a gentle fog that descends upon you. But they are dangerous. They are very dangerous, in my opinion as a non-medic.

Q17. Mr Perkins: How many companies in the world make statins?

Mr Heading: I have not kept up to date with it now but apparently it is a generic and I heard a well-known doctor here say, 'Oh, well, they are very cheap,' and I have got the figures under the Freedom of Information Act as to how much we spend on them. If napalm was cheap and botulism was cheap I probably would not take it. The insanity of saying they do not cost as much ... the on-cost of giving people statins is huge. A friend of mine in the north, his wife was put on five different statins. That is the definition to me of insanity. It should be three strikes and you are out. Didn't work, didn't work, didn't work, didn't work, didn't work. There are 12 types of cholesterol so when I ask people how many are there, they go, 'Good and bad.' They do not even give me a number. I think when I did the Parish they took some blood - nearly an arm full. We did that test. You can look at your triglycerides, you can look at 26 different elements in my blood. Only one is cholesterol. We have lost ourselves in single organ science where a short test dials out the 99 other harmful pathways; and I learnt that phrase from a guy called David Healy. He was a guest here and he wrote the books, Let Them Eat Prozac and

Pharmageddon with a 'Ph', and he said we only look for one outcome in a clinical trial but there might be 100. So you do the trial very short, a few days, and then you have somebody on a pill for life. So if you look at that I am sure I could get smoking through a clinical trial: it is a relaxant, it makes you feel good; test it for six weeks, put it on the market. You would get that through a clinical trial the way the regulators are set up. The regulators do not see the raw data. We have to see the trial data on the statins and you will find the Emperor is swimming naked, he has no clothes.

Q18. Ms Edge: So you have tried to get this trial data?

Mr Heading: I would like to get the trial data. I would like to know what is in the poor box; I would like to test it independently. Not in a Tour de France lab but in a proper independent lab or three, and then compare the results. Often they are only 2% bioavailable so they have to be 50 times stronger than you really need because the gut is very clever - 60 million years of sorting this out. So we need to test what is in it and really know what it does in the body. We are not having those honest debates from the causes of SIDS through to what is really driving the peanut allergy. We have to have those debates and this is the place to do it. We are done with the old order, we can no longer afford health.

Q20. The Chairman: Any final comments you would like to leave us with?

Mr Heading: Yes, it is actually more fun than this sounds, because I have had a hug, I had a hug in the street from a lady; she said, 'You are the statins man!' in Ramsey. I had never met her, but that was really nice. I think she meant obviously 'the anti-statins man' or 'the man who wants to debate statins', but I will take that. I have got 10 exhibits. You have received most of them and I just want to outline them so I can leave them with you, so that we have this for permanent record.

Exhibit (1) is my 'Statins - Social Affairs Committee' summary document - eight pages.

Exhibit (2), my statins four-page event handout from 25th September 2017 for my public event at the Manx Museum.

Exhibit (3) is Statins Method of Action by Dr Kathrin Kortschack, formerly of Oxford University - five pages.

Exhibit (4) is 'Derek Modral In Memory' - five pages - the husband of a friend.

Exhibit (5), Japanese statin study 'Annals of Nutrition and Metabolism' - 116 pages.

Exhibits (6), 'Food and You', a small brochure. Food is not a religion; this is only a template, a guide to healthy eating in which you might not need statins if you have a lower inflammatory diet.

Exhibit (7), 'What's on your Plate?' - the larger brochure. Both are by the Alliance for Natural Health who I am grateful to.

Exhibit (8) is 'Wellness Wednesdays', a template for topics that make us well and build natural immunity.

Exhibit (9) is 'From Framingham to Hunt 2'. It describes the collusion of 50 years of ignorant cholesterol studies that have been paid for by the statins industry.

Exhibit (10), yesterday, my Manx TV video on Thursday, 6th December: statins and HPV vaccines.

I thank you for your time and for inviting me. I cannot do this in most countries. Thank you.

The Chairman: Thank you very much for coming along, for leaving the various exhibits with us and they obviously will be on the public record. We will obviously consider what has been said in terms of our questioning of the various Departments in the future.

6. HPV vaccine carnage

If you give us a safe vaccine, we'll use it.
It shouldn't be polio versus autism.
Jenny McCarthy

My journey to full blown medical hereticism evolved slowly, with statins being a big focus early on. Thereafter, my attention was taken over by vaccines. They, more than any other religious belief, come with a full health warning of: complete debate denial, name calling, and distraction - like no other topic. People, (grown men even) have been known to leave the dinner table in my home town when the hand grenade of vaccines is chucked into 'polite' conversation. But when you actually study the science, effectiveness, contents and harms from the likes of the HPV vaccine you know you cannot simply walk on by. To literally step over 500 lifeless bodies and, yet, not one case of proven cervical cancer prevention. Worse still, I'm sure it's causing cervical cancer and much else.

Once you 'know' that you know there is no turning back; whatever the cost it is worth it. But you don't just arrive here, at this destination, on Day 1. The dis-service to the hundreds of thousands of Mothers who have seen their children harmed cannot be disregarded with 'you must be anti-vaxx', and a Conspiracy Theorist. And, likely, a baby eater, Trump supporter, anti-semite, homo-phobe and closet Brexiteer to boot.

There are times darling when Fascist simply isn't enough. Clearly those Mothers weren't Anti-Vaxx, as across the board and with total blind faith they subjected their daughters to the HPV vaccination. The doctors too - who have gone rogue - have done their own research and just want open debate, as a respectful first step. Just what does happen, post HPV vaccination, that so alarms an increasing number of medically curious doctors around the world? And not just in 80 days?

So, what exactly is this latest weapon of mass seduction - the latest must have vaccine? It's HPV, targeting the human papilloma virus, which some say can lead to cervical cancer - but it's a cancer that 99.9% of women won't get.

In those who are susceptible, the cancer can occur (rarely) around an average age of 50; that's some 35 to 40 years after vaccination. Vaccination aims to target a handful of the 100 or so HPV genotypes that account for 70% of potential cancers of the cervix. The HPV vaccine choices are Gardasil, manufactured by Merck, and Cervarix as (was) manufactured by GSK. But Cervarix harms too are still ongoing.

Dr Diane Harper was a lead Scientist and helped to get Gardasil approved. On film she states, "If you look at all the women who get an HPV infection, approximately 70% of those are going to clear that infection all by themselves within the first year, with no help from anybody - the body is going to take over and do it. Within two years about 90% of all of those HPV infections are going to clear all by themselves. After three years approximately 5% of HPV infections are going to go into a pre-cancerous lesion. The number of women who die each year is small but real. It is small because of the PAP screening program".

British GP, Dr Richard Halvorsen, authored, 'Vaccines, A Parent's Guide', and wrote a chapter on HPV vaccination entitled: 'HPV - A Vaccine Too Soon?' For context of the disease, he cites that in 2010 cancer of the cervix 'ranked' in 20th position of female cancers and that, "the exaggeration of an illness is commonplace before the introduction of a new vaccine". Dr Halvorsen champions informed patient choice and is also the founder of Baby Jabs Clinics which offers single vaccine options.

The 19 more risky cancers don't count, especially when you have a multi-billion £/$ vaccine driving the Merck share price. GSK dropped out of this now one horse 'race' a while back.

As a vaccine, Gardasil (inconveniently) is neither proven 'preventive' nor 'safe'. Never once. Nor a vaccine that contains, it seems, the ingredients which are claimed on the label - if we get into specifics and into awkward actualities. But (trigger alert) it does seem to contain numerous health wrecking balls of brain and body toxins. But only IF you look, Sherlock.

A useful place to start is the 230 pages of laboratory evidence from Corvelva in Italy. They tested four vaccines (ones, no one of my generation were given) and found mass contaminants, missing ingredients and extra bits of unidentified origin. In the HPV vaccine they found a banned amphetamine, APDB.

As pharmaceutical mis-labelling is a criminal offence, these findings have been lodged with the Treviso (Italian) Police, as a starter.

That such a medical product is injected into previously healthy young girls (and increasingly mandated for boys) who are suffering harms around the world can no longer be glossed over. Not, that is, if we call ourselves open minded, civilised, compassionate and truthful. We must look at real world evidence and science along the way - wherever it takes us. Others too have written extensively on these harms with deep dive science in support. It's not as if five HPV vaccine harms books haven't been written to date. A mere 1,800 pages that if we actually dared study we would stop the vaccine yesterday, based solely on the precautionary principle.

To increase open discussion, we held public debates on the 3rd and 4th of December, 2018 on the Isle of Man but the 'other side' hid in the bushes and almost entirely refused to attend. Though a local GP did use the words, "anti-vaxxer, fear, scare tactics and lack of science" in a public chat we had at a well attended dinner. I happened to mention, "injecting undigested protein, viral-like DNA particles, patented infertility ingredients, and neurotoxic metals" in my reply - and that the eight year, Tarsell family US legal battle confirmed the HPV vaccine did indeed cause the death of Christina Tarsell.

Sadly, there will be many more cases heading for the courts.

Japan, for one, is seeing many legal cases after their 2013 foreshortened clinical trial, due to so many harmed girls. Small countries in the Irish Sea take note.

Post-HPV vaccination harms (from Gardasil, Cervarix and Gardasil 9) and deaths have so far occurred in 55 Countries - including 'anecdotal and purely a coincidence' of course: England, USA, Sweden, France, Australia, Denmark, Canada, Japan, Mexico, Columbia, Israel, Netherlands, France, India, Argentina, Brazil, Chile, Peru, New Zealand, Spain, Portugal, Finland, Norway, Belgium, Germany, Austria, India, South Africa, Republic of Ireland, Northern Ireland, Scotland, Wales, China, Turkey, Bulgaria, Croatia, Czech Republic, Estonia, Hungary, Latvia, Lithuania, Romania, Poland, Slovenia, Slovakia, The Dominican Republic, Martinique, Philippines, Russia, Malta, Gibraltar and, my home country of the Isle of Man...

Risks Versus Benefits

The HPV vaccine is intended to reduce cervical cancer (but has never been shown to do so in a clinical trial). Only 1 in 10,000 women with HPV infection goes on to contract cervical cancer. In the US, annually, 3 women per 100,000 die of cervical cancer, while 2.3% HPV vaccinated (2,300 women per 100,000) officially suffer serious harms.

Japan ceased their HPV vaccine trials in June 2013, with legal cases of those resultant harms now in front of Tokyo and other Japanese courts. It's likely that less than one injury in 100 is reported by doctors and nurses. To do so results in, to quote them, 'professional suicide'. It's official: Where the US goes first, the world often follows. The increasing official US, CDC (Centres for Disease Control) vaccine schedule has never been clinically tested in any combination for mitochondrial or other harms.

A decade ago India was chosen for the HPV trials. Later, trial legitimacy concerns lead to an independent review by Professor of Public Health and Research Policy, Allyson Pollock of Queen Mary University, London. "We don't know if HPV vaccination works and we wouldn't ever know for 30 years - it's being rolled out on proxy measures of outcomes, not actually on reduction in deaths by cervical cancer".

Trials can miss such adverse effects, especially if the trial 'placebo' contained aluminium vaccine adjuvants - and / or the emulsifier, polysorbate 80, which is known to cause infertility.

The consent forms sent home from school, usually list 5 potential adverse effects yet the patient warning insert which accompanies the HPV vaccine, actually lists 26 adverse effects. If we always read the manufacturers warning, we'll note that the HPV vaccine "may cause seizures and/or brain damage". If you read the label, even death IS listed of this now Black Triangle Warning product. That's official.

As all vaccines act on our immune system, what happens when vaccine viruses are cultured in yeast and insects? What if there were unintended consequences crossing species, as viruses mutate from animal farm into human form?

If we think that is far fetched, we should look at Mad Cow Disease in the UK. Apparently, someone thought grinding up dead sheep suffering from scrapie disease, (double dipping) and feeding such a wondrous 'protein' to cows would be a grand idea. So how did mad cow and Mrs Thatcher make it into the same sentence, with her being a former Chemist… and Prime Minister to boot? Well, in the 1980's cows being herbivores not carnivores, as now, that's how.

'Whistle In The Wind' sure sounds like a light-hearted book - penned as it was by 2016, Doctor of The Year, Consultant Surgeon Peter Duffy, FRCS, MD. As I still believe in Santa Claus, I was stocking up with presents - especially decent books - for Christmas. The subtitle confirmed it would be a right ripping (and hacking?) yarn: 'life, death, detriment and dismissal in The NHS'. Clearly the season of peace and goodwill was now upon us. I leaned in for a cosy read, accompanying it with my own, on the hour every hour, carb fest of overindulgence. Better still, Peter was newly employed by the health service here on the Isle of Man. Clearly whistleblowing was all the rage and welcomed - 'for the times they are a changin'.

Perhaps… or maybe not.

In April 2018 I first raised the topic of world deaths and harms from HPV vaccines to the Manx Government's Whistleblowers Committee. I put forward my concerns, citing 20 Countries and three HPV books. I accompanied this evidence with a 28 points rebuttal of the Isle of Man DHSC HPV vaccine policy. In the two years since, a further two books have been published highlighting this growing scandal. Oh, and I nearly forgot further deaths and harms (and cervical cancer increases) caused by the HPV vaccine have been notified in another 35 Countries - at least. The only thing constant being change.

Then in early May, I'd appeared on Manx Radio's Mannin Line, for a discussion entitled: 'Diversifying the Manx economy'. A sort of tilt towards The Isle of Well. My topics were 'controlled' and train tracked. But at the end of May I had a private 75 minute meeting with Julie Edge, MHK, chair of the Whistleblowers Committee. We discussed harms of: HPV vaccines, statins and anti-depressants. With supporting evidence that I'd presented the month before at a public HPV vaccine harms event in Dublin, Ireland.

By June 2018 full dialogue was underway. A tynwald clerk welcomed written whistleblower evidence. I thought we were winning - naively, as it turned out. I was informed that the Public Accounts Committee was also on the case by examining the overspend at Noble's Hospital. YeeHaa! Also, my evidence would be shared, but 'the committee was not obliged to accept any evidence, nor to publish all, or any part of it - even if it has been accepted as evidence'. That's all right then. The clerk continued, 'within parliament any oral or written evidence was protected, but not when re-published'. For reasons of privacy - which I hadn't sought - they confirmed that, 'the clerk of tynwald is the data controller for the purposes of the data protection act 2002'. Phew, I knew I was in safe hands - as things would un-fold right up to and including the 5th July 2019. Better still, for correlation of cause over time, my pages of evidence would be kept indefinitely and passed to the public record office after 25 years.

By mid November, the wind was truly in our sails, as: 'The Committee looks forward to receiving your written submission about your experience of the whistleblowing process'. But three months later (email being slower on Island) on 8th February 2019, I was informed that 'unfortunately your submission of the 26th November 2018 to the Whistleblowing Select Committee does not appear to be directly connected to their remit to: review the effectiveness of the Government's current whistleblowing policy'.

The truth ball: long grass, and kicked - then punctured by a trained staffie on a lead and, later, buried.

Einstein said, 'Computers are useless they only give you answers'. We need to probe more, and be less accepting of standard, 'computer says no' mantras. Ours is a little Island but similar humans will be serving up such standard fare, in a standard letter - without much of their own independent research.

Everyone has a policy, but some have them written down, with their highly dependent Guttenberg press fired up with hot typeset, and standard prose - so it looks all official. Like. But with a crest and lots of squiggly writing and, with luck, some Latin thrown in for compliance and good measure. Probably, the Isle of Man is no different from anywhere else.

Yet, some, seem to skip their homework, preferring instead to copy a few lines from Clive the ever Clever sat over at the next desk. While others copy and paste huge swathes of standard text, using lazy shorthand, to save on the brain cells. It's done without any scrutiny nor cross referencing as to real world evidence. A surface skim instead of a deep dive.

Even if they can sense the smell of burning oil and a slipping clutch, someone else is driving their car, fully on the rev limiter. This reply on vaccines 'policy' is broadly no different to any other medical procedure. The Policy 'works' like a train firmly on tracks - it keeps chuffing around, on parallel rails, with no deviation but relies on the view from steerage class being so blurred that you can't see the broken down car on the track ahead of you. When the train does finally slow down, you are asked to look out of the windows on the left, taking in the blue lagoon seascape. A seascape which, coincidentally, occurs at the same time as the waste metal slag heap which would be apparent out of the right hand side windows, across which the bar steward has already draped rather fetching but ultra-thick curtains.

The HPV Vaccination Policy of the Isle of Man Government

follows, together with my replies (numbered 1 to 28) which are in response to their policy statement. They should be read in the context of growing legal cases across the world due to deaths and harms of HPV vaccines (Gardasil, Cervarix and Gardasil 9).

The letter below was received on 30th October 2018 from the Isle of Man Department of Health & Social Care (DHSC):

Dear Sir /Madam
Thank you for your email concerning HPV vaccination which the Chief Minister has asked my Department to respond to on his behalf. All vaccination programmes offered on the Isle of Man are based on rigorous (trials) (1) and evaluation carried out by experts (2) in their field.

Since HPV vaccines were first licensed in 2006, over 270 million doses (3) have been given worldwide, with over 8.5 million in the UK. Medicines regulatory authorities, including the Medical and Healthcare Products Regulatory Agency (UK) (4), the European Medicines Authority (5) and the World Health Organisation (6), keep the safety (7) and efficacy (8) of these vaccines under regular review (9). When vaccines are given to very large numbers of people, simply by chance (10) some will develop a medical problem around the time of the vaccine. This does not mean that the vaccine caused the problem. Detailed safety reviews (11) undertaken by the authorities listed above have not found any evidence (12) that HPV vaccine is linked to an increased risk of any condition including chronic fatigue syndrome, postural orthostatic hypotension or complex regional pain syndrome (13). There is also no evidence to link aluminium (14) an ingredient (15) in HPV and other vaccines to an increased risk of autism (16).

In the UK, there are over 3,000 new cases of cervical cancer diagnosed each year (17) and around 850 deaths (18). 99.8% of cervical cancer is caused by infection (19) and Cancer

Research UK estimates that it is also 99.8% preventable - with the HPV vaccination programme being a key part of this (20). Not all cervical cancer deaths can be prevented by the cervical screening programme for a variety of reasons - women may fail to attend for screening, they may have an aggressive cancer which develops between smears or outside the age range of the programme, and, as with any screening programme, there may be 'false negative' (21) results. The 10 year survival rate for cervical cancer is only 63% (22) and treatment can have a major impact on the quality of life and wellbeing of patients, including, for example, infertility (23).

In view of the evidence (24) outlined above, we cannot accept your statement that 'HPV vaccine is doing a lot more harm than good' (25). Full information is provided to parents (26) and to girls both as part of the consent process (27) and at the time of the vaccination (28).

My replies:

1). Rigorous programmes have not been undertaken, nor have HPV vaccine contents been studied for: toxicity, carcinogenicity, or infertility - nor have their accumulating effects on immature immune systems.

2). 'Experts in their field' remain in their isolated specialism unable and unwilling to examine vaccine effects outside of their 'vertical niche'. Harms are continually masked, via growing vaccine schedules, ignoring continued escalation of autoimmune diseases, in the young.

3). Globally, over 1 billion people smoke but a 'clinical trial' would deem smoking to be 'safe' if it had a 15 day cut off for 'evidence' of harms. This was the case in HPV vaccines 'trials' - by limiting the period of study (after which antibodies continue to have been unnaturally raised) then all 'risks' have been magically made to go away.

4). The MHRA has repeatedly failed to police major medical harms of: PiP breast implants, the Essure contraceptive device, and transvaginal mesh(es) - all were medically approved devices. MHRA failed to police Ranbaxy, a generic drug manufacturer in India supplying cheap NHS drugs.

5). Nordic Cochrane wrote to the EMA on 26th May 2016, stating maladministration by the EMA, regarding HPV vaccine harms. These harms have not been adequately investigated, nor resolved.

6). The WHO states clearly: any parent who does not wish their child to receive the HPV vaccine, should keep their child off school on vaccination day. How is that in any way an 'informed consent'?

7). Safety is claimed despite Indian trial deaths, and a later review by Professor Allyson Pollock. Trial harms were substantially masked by use of an aluminium adjuvant comparator, not an inert placebo.

8). Efficacy has never been proven in a clinical trial. An assumed, surrogate end point of CIN lesion 'reduction' is assumed to be proof of cancer elimination. Any claims of cancer prevention are false.

9). A regular review has never been undertaken. (In the US, Health & Human Services directorate was mandated to undertake a biennial review, but has not done so, on 15 occasions since 1987).

10). Simply by 'chance' was a mantra used by the lobbyists for: lead in paint, tobacco harms, deaths due to Vioxx and Prozac; while HIV blood tainting is currently going through UK courts after 30 years.

11). Detailed safety reviews have never investigated harms

from the official Yellow Card system. There is no follow up process in place to respect the view of the patient voice. Less than 1 in 100 harms are reported (see the Harvard Pilgrim study). Adverse events viewed as an inconvenience.

12). 'Not found any evidence' ignores: the excessively high MHRA's Yellow Card system, AHVID (Association of HPV Vaccine Injured Daughters) and Time For Action: which expose repeated, decade long harms which are unparalleled for any vaccine.

13). POTS (Postural Orthostatic Tachycardia Syndrome), and CRPS (Complex Regional Pain Syndrome) are highly HPV vaccine correlated. Japan has ongoing, 'common symptom', Court cases of harms to 2,000 girls following their prematurely aborted trials of HPV vaccines in 2013.

14). To link aluminium to autism: see the film: Injecting Aluminium by Prof Chris Exley. As the foremost global expert in aluminium toxicity, he had been initially sceptical of the causal link of aluminium to autism - but he now does, following 20 years of detailed research and brain autopsies.

15). Vaccine ingredients: include HPV strains 16 and 18 for 'cancer' but 2014 research by Dr Vanessa Hearnden found that only 2.2% were 16 or 18 strain matched in oral strain analysis in her study of 702 University of Sheffield students.

16). Increased rate of autism: The US, CDC (Centres for Disease Control) confirms that autism has risen from 1 case in 10,000 in 1985, rising to 1 in 36 in 2018. As there is an absence of thirty year old people with autism, it is not better monitoring but likely to be: earlier, closer, and ever more, vaccines.

17). Cervical cancers diagnosed: ignores several lifestyle, contributory causes. The last thing the NHS ever targets… causes. High risks driving cervical cancer include: 1) smoking,

2) poor nutrition, 3) 11 or more oral sexual partners or, 4) six or more vaginal, or anal sex, partners.

18). Around 850 deaths: every death is a personal tragedy. While in context, cervical cancer is the 20th least likely female cancer, and vaccine harms are 2,300 / 100,000, while deaths are 3 / 100,000.

19). 99.8% caused by infection: odd karyotypes of 'cancer' cells... (where only 1 in 10,000 with HPV infection actually develops cancer): Dr Peter Duesberg and Norma Erickson dispute that HPV virus is actually cancer 'causing', but is a bystander, the fireman at the scene of a fire - he didn't cause it.

20). 99.8% preventable while HPV vaccination is key: Cervical cancers have reduced over decades by over 90%, due to highly accurate low cost, minimal harms, PAP screening. So, with no clinical evidence of the HPV vaccine preventing cancer, remains a 40 year bet on potential outcomes.

21). Maybe 'false negative' results: But a greater issue is of 'false positives'. (Denmark, Canada and Sweden confirm that by studying over 30 years, counterintuitively breast screening is net harmful - with unscreened women living longer, due to incidence of unreal cancers being wrongly 'identified'.

22). Ten year survival is only 63%: But only using the 1939 legally mandated protocols of: radiation, chemotherapy or surgery (cut, burn or poison). While ignoring the health of the bodily 'terrain' to rebuild and protect the immune system.

23). Infertility, caused by treatment: Of greater concern are HPV vaccine ingredients of borax and polysorbate 80 (Tween 80) the former a patented cockroach killer, the latter patented for infertility. A study by Gayle Delong, studied 8 million US Women, aged 25 - 29 and confirmed their declining fertility, between 2007 and 2014, post HPV vaccination.

24). The evidence: what is cited lacks scientific basis, as is based only on extrapolated CIN3 lesion reduction, not proven efficacy against actual cervical cancers. The HPV vaccine contains known toxic ingredients, has negligible strain matching, with harms that far outweigh any 'reduction' of cancers.

25). DHSC denial 'that HPV vaccine is doing more harm than good' ignores evidence in 52 Countries from lawyers, medics, and concerned parents who just seek answers for the harms to their children.

26). Full information provided to parents: is not provided by a paper based form, rather than easy to access, digital web links showing adverse effects / vaccine contents. (Nurse coercion doesn't help).

27). Part of the consent process to girls: real world discussion with girls is that they do not know what they are signing up for, being "disease-mongered" to a very rare cancer, to quote a Manx GP.

28). Full information at the time of the vaccine: there is never full discussion of relative risks versus benefits. The instilling of fear predominates: supported by Pharma advertising, and NHS promotion.

As far back as 2009, in the US, Dr Scott Ratner and his wife, also a Physician, blamed HPV vaccination for their daughter's sudden onset life debilitating illness.

Across the world other eminent doctors like Dr Louise Brinth, Professor Peter Gøtzsche, Dr Bart Classen and Dr Stephanie Seneff have all raised serious concerns over HPV vaccination harms.

Legal cases of HPV vaccination harms are also underway in:

UK, Ireland, Denmark, Sweden, Spain, France and Italy, as well as over 300 cases of (mass) adverse effects in young women in Carmen de Bolivar, Columbia.

By 2011, the US FDA's VAERS (Vaccine Adverse Events Reporting System) had already received 18,727 reports of adverse effects following HPV vaccination, with a total of 2,799 classified as 'serious'.

In June 2013 Japan suspended HPV vaccination, due to numerous reported adverse effects and in 2018 a law suit was brought by Class Action Plaintiffs in the Tokyo District Court.

As for real world, risk context - studies published in JAMA (The Journal of The American Medical Association) confirm that long-term smokers have a more than three fold increased risk of developing cancer of the cervix. Eating a poor diet too is also a major contributory factor - again due to a constantly compromised immune system. We should look at education of cancer causes.

The 'trials' were deeply flawed: often they used only one dose, selected only healthy volunteers, were 'light' on fully informed consent, and dismissed the 49% of trialists with 'new medical conditions...'

Further evidence is offered by US based Geneticist and Pathologist (formerly of Yale University) Dr Sin Hang Lee. He is concerned at HPV 'viral like' particle DNA which, when combined with aluminium adjuvants, leads to brain injuries.

Dr Lee's findings have been supported by French Organic Chemist, Dr Laurent Bélec. Dr Lee appeared before the Scottish Parliament in 2015 to share his concerns of the aluminium adjuvant, in the HPV vaccine, as it's a known human brain harming neurotoxin.

The slow release of HPV vaccine ingredients IS leading to severe harms: heavy and irregular periods, brain damage, infertility, appendicitis, constant joint pain, extreme tiredness (despite 15 hours of sleep), seizures, and heart beat dysfunction. Despite going through a tortuous process, the US National Vaccine Injury Compensation Program has (so far) paid out compensation to 49 Girls due to HPV vaccination. The first case proving death due to Gardasil, of Christina Tarsell, has been determined in the US Vaccine Injuries Court - and this followed an eight year legal battle.

Monday 3rd December 2018, was a day of enlightenment for me. We had lunch with a Manx GP; 'we' being me and Dr Sherri Tenpenny. Despite the US vaccine compensation fund being in existence for a mere 32 years our GP friend had not heard of it; so, clearly, the $4+ billion paid out to date didn't matter either.

In the evening at the Manx Museum, Dr Chris Exley, of Keele University (known as 'Mr Aluminium' to many) a world expert on aluminium - a subject he's been researching in detail for over thirty years - gave a fantastic talk.

Aluminium has become a part of everyday life in the modern era and is used in the manufacture of pots and pans, lightweight engineering and also for vaccine adjuvants - it is these adjuvants which 'excite' an immune response. But immune response does not confirm immunity. It is simply a measuring stick - a bit like an abacus. But it seems that aluminium has no biological function in any organism and is neither essential nor beneficial for human life - whilst it has also never been tested for human toxicity. If we can digress, up an awkward cul-de-sac.

There is science based research in the film, 'Injecting Aluminium', from Cinema Libre Studios, highlighting hundreds of sick patients in France - a story replicated in many other countries. Many cite the evidence that silica has kept aluminium out of living things for almost all of evolution (bar the last century) - perhaps it is the greatest story still waiting to be told? The film confirmed the shocking reality of aluminium as an unsafe, untested, vaccine adjuvant.

It's only relevance to sound medical science was because its name begins with the letter A. As in, 'a' 90 years experiment - with no sound evidence - that it is safe to be injected into a human, or animal body. It's toxic, so it's not, in summary.

Tuesday 4th December 2018 and time to let Dr Sherri shine, to present her 30,000 hours of vaccine research. First, up in Ramsey, then later at lunchtime in Douglas. We nearly didn't get to Douglas on time. Earlier I had to literally prize Sherri away from one hugging Mum who said, "but who are my boys going to marry?" Those both being unvaccinated, healthy, brainy bright and bushy tailed. With the infertile female population gene pool growing by the day the odds are shortening. Seek and you shall find - if you dare look.

I will defer now to the 'top of the pyramid' - the hierarchy of the medical establishment - and turn to Professor Heidi Larson, Founder Director of the Vaccine Confidence Project, who on 3rd December 2019, presented to the WHO (World Health Organisation) Global Vaccine Safety Summit in which she said, "The other thing that's a trend and an issue is not just confidence in providers but confidence of health care providers. We have a very wobbly health professional frontline that is starting to question vaccines and the safety of vaccines, when the frontline professionals are starting to question… or they don't feel like they have enough confidence about the safety to stand up to the person asking them the questions. I mean most medical school curriculums, even nursing curriculums, I mean, in medical school you're lucky if you have half a day on vaccines. Never mind keeping up to date with all this".

At the same WHO conference Dr Soumya Swaminathan - its Chief Scientist - who is a 'paediatrician by training' from India, said, "There are the sceptics and the critics and people who will constantly be pointing out the risk of side effects and making associations and so on. That is to say, people who point out constantly that vaccination entails the risk of side effects".

She blamed a low uptake for the HPV vaccine in India on critics who associated the vaccine with adverse events and deaths, that according to her were due to other causes. "I think we cannot emphasize the fact that we really don't have very good monitoring systems in many countries, and this adds to the miscommunication and misapprehensions because we're not able to give clear-cut answers when people ask about the deaths that have occurred due to a particular vaccine, and this always gets blown up in the media. One should be able to give a very factual account of what exactly has happened and what the cause of deaths are; but in most cases there is obfuscation at that level and therefore there's less and less trust in the system".

She went on, "Putting in place the mechanisms, to be able to monitor and detect vaccine associated adverse events is important because just as many times adverse events caused by pharmaceutical products were only identified years after the drug had been licenced and marketed to the public, unexpected things could arise after vaccination, and one always has to be prepared". She concluded to her colleagues, "So I think risk is always there, and I think the population needs to understand that and feel confident that mechanisms are being put in place to study some of those things".

But not too closely. Obviously.

7. Catching on to cancer

If we get kids eating right, we could decrease
cancer rates by 90 percent.
Joel Fuhrman

I appreciate not everyone will be interested necessarily in the HPV Vaccine but there is surely one area of medicine that EVERYONE would be; and that is cancer.

Cancer used to be something of a rare occurrence but it has a history of speaking with a forked tongue. So we are struggling to find our way home. Especially as in the US, the $160 billion annual cost of cancer 'care' makes it an unholy juggernaut of an industry. For each patient the average treatment costs over $100,000. Clearly, a 'gold' (standard) treatment for some - with a platinum bonus ball and two Mercs on the drive.

If we go back to the future, it's worth revisiting some cancer 'truths' of six decades ago; back then experts told us: 'cigarette smoking does not cause cancer'. That was said in 1958, by the CDC (Centres for Disease Control). They are now holders, conveniently, of many profitable patents across 'health' industry sectors to aid our health - including one for the HPV vaccine - to 'cure' cervical cancer.

Around the World countless kind people are raising money for and giving thought to those with cancer, especially each 4th February, that being World Cancer Day. The 'War on Cancer' was a term coined by US President Richard Nixon in 1971. Yes, that Richard, aka: Tricky, as in, "I am not a crook" Nixon.

We're now several decades on and several hundred billion (with a B) dollars / pounds / euros in, with this cancer saviour. So let's see how far Dickie has helped propel us. Although, to be brutally honest, it seems we haven't (actually) progressed much in terms of reduced mortality from cancer. That being the key statistic not life 'extended', if the diagnosis was false to start with. To quote the BBC's Blackadder, referring to first World War carnage, "Baldrick, we've advanced about as far as an asthmatic ant carrying two heavy bags of shopping". If that.

With that in mind, imagine if you (or Dickie) were told, 'it's the policy man', so we're steered away from factual scrutiny. Then again, we can't find what we don't look for - in cancer, or in any other disease.

Back in May 2019, I heard a British doctor present a story which didn't quite make the front, nor side page, in the MSM (main stream media). It seems that unintended consequences of the British Police tetra radio system have suffered from radio silence - where harms are concerned. Perhaps, the big knob has set it that way. As evidence of harms became apparent, (head and neck) cancers on the same side as the 'talking broach' radio - that being a coincidental location - 'ipsilateral' cancer. The officially sanctioned solution, of course, was to disband the police occupational health unit. It's policy man. Nice. Along with some lame stream, not main stream, non reporting. In cancer, it seems, that truth is not exactly a fair cop, is it?

If we follow the cancer money, it also makes sense to follow the almost non money too - such as a 10 pence per day cancer treatment, currently being trialled. That's what happens when you combine Vitamin C with Antibiotics, as suggested by a nine year old. Yes, really. The trial is a 'cheap as chips' remedy, via a Salford University researcher's managed trial in Italy. Why are such trials targeting cancer tumours being undertaken in Italy? Ease of process, and cost, that's why. Some say you also need an international mindset by Canadian Professor Michael Lisanti and his Italian Wife, Dr Federica Sotgia. Why they are focused on the cut price end of treatment is anyone's guess but, in a word, likely it is: conscience.

Meanwhile, the average US Oncologist is trousering (a wallet busting ski lodge in Vermont) $300,000 per year. For them business - sorry, treatment - as usual is buying chemo wholesale while selling it retail to patients: the artist formerly known as people and photogenic kids (but no skis). It's noted that some 70% of oncologists' income, Stateside, comes from selling chemo drugs… the remaining 30% from sick bucket and wig sales.

Finally vicar, I'm dying to ask, "Do I have cancer because I lack chemo?".

More so, as the eggheads say that chemo blocks our most powerful cancer repair cells, our innate 'cancer macrophages'. That's our inbuilt cancer Big Eaters to you and me.

Suddenly it seems prostates are back in vogue yet, for a while, prostates were given the press equivalent of the bums rush. So much so that Vogue magazine in the UK covered prostate cancer on 5th February 2010 and suddenly, more than seven years later, on 25th August 2017 - when their Aussie cousins went 'down under' too, on the topic.

Vesuviusly, it's hot news; as if someone handed them a script to spout. Collectively. TV personalities, and authors are on the prostate news. I've counted four this last week, all suffering from that same affliction - one that brings a watery eye to most men of a certain age, that is: prostate problems. These popular, trusty 'personalities' ranged in age from 60 to over 80 - so, no potential patient voice, and cheque book, is left behind. A male 'problem' that we all want to know more about, an issue that, as we age, we can't fully outrun. Or can we? Prostate cancer is more possibly a thing we are to die with than from. How can that be deduced? Well, by Richard Ablin, no less. 'Who's he?', the average GP/MD might well ask.

Dr Richard Ablin felt driven to write his seminal book, 'The Great Prostate Hoax', after 17 years of hearing about fake 'science'. Dr Ablin, it could be noted, is the leading prostate scientist, largely credited with inventing the PSA test. But a 'test' that was never intended, by him, to be an accurate prostate cancer marker 'test'. Over 20 years since its inception, and FDA approval, it has racked up $60 billion in sales. It seems that some have been able to give up their paper round, while flogging a $60 million per week, fear factor based 'test' for the older man. Which seems more than a bit below the belt.

When we think about it clearly and without disease-mongering, if some tests are not accurate then 'length of life lived after a diagnosis' becomes, in reality, pretty irrelevant. When Dr Ablin was interviewed by Scripps Research Institute founder, Dr Eric Topol, he stated that 'his' standard PSA test is 78% inaccurate. An important word is 'in' when it precedes accurate.

So, only one in five men may get an accurate 'diagnosis'; with a four fifths error rate that's rather light on precision, Sherlock. But, truth be told, less precision leads to more incision on the operating table. Being of an age that a doctor, if ever he sees me, might enquire if I would like a PSA test - he may just be told where he should stick it. Greased or otherwise.

In March 2017 I met a clever specialist who'd helped launch a US cancer drug. It wasn't so much the deep dive science but the method by which the drug actually works, that caught my attention. This 'ground-breaking' cancer drug has a claimed patient oral bio-availability of 4% in a fasted state, a slightly better 9% in a fed state, but a whopping 16% bio-availability when consumed alongside... grapefruit juice. You read that right, 84% (at best) isn't bio-available. All that, to help turbo-charge drug effectiveness with a starting yearly price of only $115,000 per patient. So, you can quadruple its effectiveness simply by purchasing a 55 pence grapefruit. And, no, I'm not taking the 'pith' - but someone is.

Cancer specialist and geneticist, Dr Thomas Seyfried, has researched prostate cancers up close and personal. He believes, like many of us, that dietary-led, fat burning ketosis holds the key to avoiding many 'deadly' cancers. Sounds a bit too diet and habits, for the scalpel brigade - but there you go.

Let's also tip toe through the tulips of evidence that excessive carbs/sugars/glucose feeds the escalation in cancer cell growth. So, what happens when you starve the cells of glucose? They die, that's what. What if cancer dis-ease was broken down to its most basic of parts? We'd see it was only: 1) a toxin and 2) a lack.

What if cancer causes have not just a physical component but emotional ones too - those not so visible triggers, of fear porn news, and 5G bombardment? What if the toxic shocks leads to emotional trauma? In the cancer as a meat model, spirit and emotion doesn't get a look in. Not just what are you eating but also, riding in tandem, with the 'what's eating you brigade'.

What if, in part, there's disruption to the energy source that powers our body? The hidden thing which animates us, as 24/7 wired, water body human meat sticks? An enormous research wedge is spent annually on genomics, looking with ever greater reductionism into every cellular nook and cranny. But it seems that when Sherlock The Scientist decoded us lot, we had only 23,000 genes - not the 100,000 genes that Dr Watson was expecting. Oh dear! In fact, very dear was that $3 billion human genome project.

As two legged types we seem impressive until you realise that in the gene genie stakes we nestle well below the water flea who gets by with 31,000 genes. It's likely their extra genes are needed for swimming, and for being more than handy at after dinner Sudoku. But back to cancer 101. What if the size of our jeans - not the number of our genes - is actually a more accurate, less reductionist, contributor?

The rear view mirror is not always a good place to start when driving, but it is when examining cancer causes. We need to back up historically, paddle up stream, to go against the $low flow of cancer ideas - which currently have us stuck in a whirlpool vortex. A mere 90 years ago, we were more on the money... with cancer causes, way before it had become a very profitable industry. The 1930's was a time when cancer was a 1 in 100 occurrence, not the 1 in 3 people disease it is now - age weighted. That's a reliable start; age weighted. If we review the 1930's work of Nobel Prize Winner, Dr Otto Warburg, who stated, "Cancer is, above all, a sugar fermentation process" then we might just find our way home from the whirlpool.

Our well intentioned focus on 'cures' has sadly consigned real causes to that waste bin of underfunded and possibly awkward investigative research. Yet, we should revisit original work for actual cancer causing evidence.

So cancer is a metabolic disease. Yet, what has the modern Western diet adopted? Well: grains and carbohydrates and factory made sugars - all major fermentation and inflammation promoters. Yet, still, in cancer hospitals, such as the Christie Hospital in Manchester, in patient and public areas they only sell sugary, highly processed fast foods. Profitably. Let's also ignore too, the recent spate of cancer advertorials on British television. Highlighting the need for more and more and (yet) more funding. Back to basics would be more fruitful.

Most cancers take decades to grow, yet in the US some 70% of prostate cancer patients elect for surgery within 48 hours of getting a diagnosis. Go figure, after someone has: gone finger. While those surgically treated versus those untreated have the same life expectancy. Neat. Death has always been a useful, if

110

final (and pretty accurate) measure of life.

Peter Starr is a filmmaker and had been going on swimmingly with his life and work. That was until his airbag of life went off, bringing him to a shuddering halt. If that's not too below the belt, Peter. In fact, that was exactly where his personal airbag was located - below his belt. Step up, Dr Glum, who opined, "Mr Starr, you have prostate cancer".

So started Peter on his journey and a film series, where he outlined the shocking evidence of the prostate cancer 'as business' model. But Peter was not one of those 'quick to the surgeon' prostate patient types. Instead, he consulted 56 prostate experts (medical doctors and PhD's) around the world, and well over a decade later he is still spreading his healing message via a DVD series under his Educational Foundation. It helped that Peter is an accomplished filmmaker who had the drive and, dare we say, intact balls to help educate us. That way, with a stiffer resolve, your Wife also gets to appreciate your newfound health - above and below the belt.

But if you don't ignore causes you can't get patients on the operating table; manufacturing a disease is a good start to the: cut, burn, poison, treatment industry. It's a profitable - sorry, caring - industry; one wedded to the deeply enshrined 1939 British Cancer Act, prescribing cancer 'solutions' such as: surgery, chemo or radiation. A treatment by law, from just 81 years ago, a time before Granddad was born. Now, if someone turned up in a 1939 car I'd say, "How quaint, let's go for a 40 miles per hour spin, maybe 50 max, as I'm feeling frisky". But if someone offered that white knuckle, white coated ride with no seat belts, no anti-lock brakes, no airbag, nor safety glass wind-screen I'd say, "I'll pass".

Cancer therapy doesn't advance because that's not where the money is. Nor where the disease was in 1939. Adolf.

Speaking of money, up at the profitable end of the earnings league are 'chemo' drugs, with profits that keep stock markets buoyant. Take your pick on currency but chemo costs tens of thousands of pounds / dollars / euros per round. As medical bills are the biggest cause of individual bankruptcies in the US, let's stick in dollars. For simplicity.

Bubonic plague once banged at our door begging to be let in - it came and went, mysteriously, without our interference apart from not drinking our own urine, not eating rotten food, nor drinking water from lead pipes. One day 'chemo' will be like that too. In time, we will ask just how did 'chemo' become fêted as a remotely orthodox, lawful, cancer 'solution'? Something invented out of WW1 mustard gas? C'mon guys, perhaps we can do better.

Researching how tumours grow would be a good place to start; one to better understand the decades long growth of our prostate 'friend'. With the comparison of: surgery, chemo or watchful waiting, which option wins? Which 'solution' has less 'deaths after a decade'? That being a fairly relevant measure, although all cause mortality, is likely, a far better one. Where death is concerned it is the (counter-intuitive) watchful waiting that is often the much less invasive but more successful option. If we examine other evidence we also find that it supports the benefits of an alkaline inducing diet and other 'prostate positive' lifestyle changes. That 'active' watchful waiting actually tops the pile and leaves our below the belt functions still, well, functioning.

With Breast Screening Programme lessons from the US, Canada and Denmark, the Swiss were compelled to stop future breast screening programmes in 2014. The mammography harms were simply too high for any benefits gained. That was due to excessive false positives in finding 'cancers' that weren't real, such as the upsold: Duct Carcinomas In Situ (DCIS) which, in most cases, weren't actually cancers, just mis-named and mis-identified. Such 'cancers' that, given time, were mostly found to have regressed harmlessly on their own without treatment.

John Bailar was the Editor of the US Cancer Journal. In 1985 he stated "If we are to effectively prevent cancers we will have to change our lives". He continued, "we have brought some of the best minds to the problem, but despite our best shot it's time to admit it hasn't worked". He stated that a change of the kind he was proposing would mean a massive disruption in ideas, in the research community, and in the businesses that support that community. In other words, 'vested interest' inertia - or a lack of momentum that rarely best serves the patient. Such as: is breast screening actually, in fact, net harmful? So, if some cancers are not real, are five year survival figures really a true measure?

In November 2016 the film, 'The C Word' by Virgil Films, started doing the rounds at conferences. It focused on the causes, finance and care of cancer. Most importantly, what we can do to help ourselves and for those we love. The current epidemic is best captured in these words: Stress, Toxins, Exercise and Diet. STED, as an acronym, will be at the centre of my mind forever. Well done to the filmmakers doing it for truth, not profit.

Away from powerful drugs, hyperbaric oxygen is increasingly called in to aid immune system support, a natural way to boost our mitochondrial batteries of 'life' energy. Our biggest need is a return to true health; to up-regulate our enzymes to burn fats as fuel as part of a diet driven body balance homeostasis. These valiant researchers may have also discovered there is little money in this approach. Just saying.

But are we being unfair on science as a business - sorry, solution - model? 'Of Mice and Men' was penned by the great John Steinbeck. It focused on the US Great Depression of, coincidentally, the 1930's. Nearly a century on, we still (depressingly) use mice as our cancer testing model as they are identical to us, in every way. Well nearly professor, as they have 97% of the same DNA as us. So what of the mouse that roars with cancer - that decades long 'gold standard' of animal trial models. What if those mouse trials actually involved a fair bit of monkey, cow and pig business too? So, let's look at our (near) identical twin, Mickey M. The mouse can make vitamin C but we can't - so they won't catch scurvy if they sail across the Atlantic on their summer holidays with Cliff Richard. On average, at best, their lifespan is three years but clearly not, if they repeatedly spill a pal's pint in a Glasgow pub. Scientists can grow a cancer to be one third of the mouse's body weight, while they also don't vomit - the be-tumoured mouse that is, not the less caged, hairy eared, poor dress sensed urbane scientist.

Though, to be fair, mice do have two spare legs compared with us, but... they can't drive, nor talk, nor open a bank account, nor use a mobile phone (whilst driving). It seems like they're pretty much utterly identical to us, then? Apart from eating a totally different diet, having different teeth, far less organs, different enzymes, proteins and brain sizes. Oh, and yet, while catching and passing on lots of different animalistic diseases... Squeak up at the back. There must be many other ways in which we're identical to a mouse? As in, genetically 97% 'identical' - yeah right! Identical, then, seems to be a medically 'fluid', trans-fact, post-truth, word. In short, it IS the little things, professor.

As Easy As: A, B, C. Not a line you'll see anytime soon but perhaps by 2050 we will hear, 'Anything But Chemo' as a more effective, less painful and toxic way to treat cancer - one becoming mainstream. Speaking as a non-medic, we can dare to dream. That dream would be that one day we'll look back on 2020 just as we do to the days of eight pint blood-letting, ducking stools for witches and open sewers. Along with surgeons who didn't wash their hands before birthing a baby, not even after their trip to the mortuary to do autopsies.

In short, back in the good old days, we were ignor-ant of evidence. Once upon a time they were all medical norms, the Gold 'standard of care' to keep us 'healthy'. Just as lead pipes, asbestos, DDT, and glyphosate were the norms - hiding the unknown unknowns Dr Rumsfeld.

In June 2018 The Independent, no less, trumpeted: 'most women with breast cancer can avoid toxic chemo, major trial finds'. A newspaper that being 'independent' should perhaps probe and prod, with awkward questions - being non attached to the easy, but unchecked, mantras. Of others. To stand aside from, as in, to be: truly independent. So there we have it: 'chemo' and toxic in the same sentence in a National British broadsheet.

Not so much for The Times, but for The Independent - 'the times, they are a changin'. Fittingly at last, some might say. I've omitted the word 'therapy' which appeared after 'chemo' in the article. Toxic, somehow, seems to negate that (with apologies to the author, Health Correspondent, Alex Matthews-King) for butchering his piece. The Danish 17 year breast study highlights significant over-treatment due to 'false positive' inaccuracies in identifying non-malignant 'tumours'.

That 3rd June 2018 article had, of course, a genetic slant to it, mentioning the HER2 receptor on which the trial was focused. They also proclaimed screening which might better identify cancers and how to avoid toxic chemotherapy. Wow, they escaped the script sensors with that one. But, earlier screening, to find self disappearing non-cancers, is not the winning solution. C.O.U.N.T.E.R. I.N.T.U.I.T.I.V.E.L.Y... before anyone fires up the gallows, rope and lynching party.

Chemo-'therapy' is used to shrink a cancer tumour before

radiation or surgery. As a treatment it came into vogue 100 years ago. Wafting gently on the breeze, as if a gossamer winged butterfly, out of WWI trenches. A place where the stench of mass death was everywhere. If that's not over the top, Major. Yet, to date, it hasn't actually had that many bragging rights, except with Major Monty, who was slow on the front line - while he finished his cigar. And port.

So, what if tumour shrinkage is the wrong measure? That would be a bit like saying 'look how small my weeds are' while not noticing that the roses just aren't growing anymore. Then the weeds come back again and again and again - terrains are like that. What happens if chemo creates stemness? What is stemness? Well, it's defined as encouraging cancer stem cells to return with vengeance and virulence, having lurked around until conditions are just 'right' to come back but, some say, much stronger. That's stemness.

Perhaps their return is more likely to occur if three 'ideal' conditions are in play: 1) a chemo-compromised immune system; 2) an oxygen and nutritional lack, and; 3) a body conditioned to sugar expectancy. Perhaps it's all a modern conspiracy, while ignoring Otto Warburg, from 90 years ago. He really focused on the C words: Cancer and Causes.

Would Oncologists Use Chemo On Their Families? - A friend on Island, for years, administered chemo to her patients and attributes her serious allergies to the aerosol chemo that she used, under prescribed 'protocols'.

Meanwhile, coincidentally, a chemo spillage is treated as a US hazardous material incident and has special clean up procedures (and protocols).

Another former Nurse, and parliament member, in my home country has said she, "would never have chemo".

Just why are tens of billions of cancer research dollars so heavily skewed towards genetics when, by examining identical twins over decades, we can see that genetics drive 'at very best...' 10% of the causes of deaths. Genetics load your gun but - and it's a big butt - your environment pulls the trigger. Quite. Genetics is, in major reality, not your destiny; not in 90% of cancer cases anyway. The main drivers are poor lifestyle habits, toxins and diets conflicting with our bodily proteins which are far more abundant than our genes. Proteins are what express our genes.

For screening out loud, Nurse - What remains unmentioned, independently, unprofitably, are decades long screening inaccuracies. In breast cancer, if we look at DCIS 'cancers' (Duct Carcinomas In Situ) we see something that is considered by many oncologists to be a 'non' cancer. If we look, they are a modern invented 'problem'. But, by now, DCIS has been so fully ramped up the fear slope - a case of dis-ease inflation, if ever there was one.

In 2014 Switzerland dropped new breast screening. The Swiss have found their experience replicated the evidence found, for decades of analysis as seen in Sweden, Denmark and Canada.

The unscreened live longer.

Finally, with education, the disease-mongering and chemo industries might just be on the decline. Big hooray. Now that's an actual honest 'therapy' that we can believe in. With less being more. By 2050, hopefully, 'Anything But Chemo' will be as easy as A, B, C. But for now we'll just give the chemo 'industry' a less than healthy D minus, while insisting that, finally, we keep abreast of real evidence.

In March 2013, I attended the European Congress of Radiology in Vienna. Nothing special in that, but what I heard there changed me forever. A presenting Radiologist declared, "breast screening, is 53% accurate"... No one gasped, no one refuted it. More surprisingly no one fainted. Some of us found that chilling. Having my one O level (in Maths) I could only think: what IF my Wife is in the 47% brigade? But as she doesn't have her breasts screened that was unlikely. It's worth noting that a coin toss does nearly as well - that's right, tossers can win sometimes, sadly. Time to brush off a library copy of: relative versus absolute risk, too.

While in Vienna, I also took part in a medical 'press button when ready' quiz, beating most who were there. It was depressing to realise there was something rotten in the state of Austria. Later, trying to be upbeat, I phoned my ministerial handler at the time, while taking out a mortgage for the Austria to Island mobile call.

Later, the mood was lifted by Harvard Medical Professor Giles Boland, who championed 4pm daily, group learning, radiology sessions. Everyone from trainee to fully fledged professor was expected to review the images of the day, to say how they saw the visual evidence. No punch nor rank was pulled, the ebb and flow of patient centric, decision making, trumped all. A revolutionary concept and one that Giles tried to get adopted across the US. But he was met with the stoniest of stone walls of inertia. Over 90% of hospitals he wrote to never replied and of those who did only 2% had a peer review of radiology processes. Life and death process decisions, at that. In an aircraft anyone from the most junior to the most seasoned captain can effectively ground the fleet. In radiology, guys and girls they are flying blind, and single pilot, who gets eye strain and brain fade, just like everyone else.

The Swedes are an inventive bunch. So far they've brought us: the telephone handset, the three pointed seat belt, the implantable pacemaker and, yes, explosives, lest they be too good... Professor Catharina Svanborg of Lund University is focused on medical innovation and specifically on human breast milk containing fatty acids that kill cancer cells. First up, urinary bladder cancer. An interesting start but, with luck, one day (when cancers aren't called by their organ name) our internal orchestra may be encouraged to play all the instruments at the same time. In tune.

Have we been here before? As this research builds on the findings of Otto Warburg who, in the 1920's, identified glucose fermentation as a driver of cancer cell growth. Dr Warburg was awarded the Nobel Prize for his work, a prize instituted by... Alfred Nobel. Circling back to the future, Mr Nobel was also the inventor of dynamite. He was not only Swedish but another unconventional thinker and who later in his life, morphed into a peace promoter. Give that man a prize.

They say London buses take a while to appear and then suddenly two come along at once. It's a bit like that with the 'Vitamin C is effective to treat cancer' mantra. In April 2017 two Universities, on both sides of The Pond, came along with successful clinical trials. Intravenous Vitamin C has an ability to treat cancer due to its ability to restrict angiogenesis (new blood vessel growth) in tumours and real world evidence is building. But the Vitamin C cancer treatment idea is not new.

Three decades ago the wheels temporarily came off the Vitamin C Cancer Bus, despite the best efforts of Nobel Prize Winner, Dr Linus Pauling. Such 'free radical thinkers' usually wait a lifetime to see their ideas escape out of the lab. Maybe we really do now have a more welcoming environment, especially with multiple cancer rates at an all-time high.

The University of Iowa is the latest to announce results of a relatively inexpensive approach to treating brain and lung cancer tumours. "These two diseases really haven't had a significant improvement in outcomes for the last two or three decades" says Bryan Allen, UI Assistant Professor of Radiation Oncology and an author on the study. "This is a well-tolerated, very cost-effective treatment, and it may significantly improve patient outcomes".

Meanwhile, also published in 2017, in Oncotarget, was a University of Salford study lead by Professor Michael P. Lisanti with Dr Gloria Bonuccelli. They found that: 'Vitamin C is up to 10 times more effective at stopping cancer cell growth than some drugs'. Now that's more than juicy - it's fuel for a whole fleet of buses. A new era and one increasingly where the patient is the fully involved driver.

It's not just fruits. Veggies too help prevent colorectal and other cancers, with full-on PubMed cited research. Cancer reducing phyto-nutrients, like cabbage and broccoli, lead the 'charge of the green brigade'.

For guys in the fight against testicular cancer apparently you should get your hands on your nuts and seeds: a daily intake of those tasty legumes is cited to help slow the rapid release of dietary sugars - depriving tumours of their chosen sweet foods. Now that, quite naturally, is tasty.

It's as if we think more of our pets than our fellow humans. Although you can still get thimerosal laced rabies vaccines on the Island of Man so we're not there yet. 'Supervet' Noel Fitzpatrick is doing what I think is a sterling job on TV repairing, surgically, the post vax leg carnage. But why has he never ventured forth as to the cause? In January 2020 he was deep diving into removing an infection, and the titanium plate had to come out as well. If titanium poisons humans, what if our four legged friends react too? Dare we ask, if we could talk to the animals, Dr Dolittle? Well, not on screen anyway - unless I missed that episode. Please, can we find a fat bloke down the pub and take him for a drink, to engage in some deep dive heavy chatting, and later tell me what he says: when we ask what really drives cancer in young puppies in their fastest growing stage? A mere 10% genetic cause is my bet...

Today, 30th January 2020, an email has plopped on the mat. It caught my eye as it headlined, 'If you're over 45 then your prostate is the size of a lemon'. The sender (and unsubscribe) button highlighted their Salt Lake City address. I was thinking, do they think I was a moron? In case I had dozed off, it showed a walnut and lemon sized comparison image - hold the front page. As my current age puts me 17 years into the fruit zone, I'm off to check if I've, unluckily, a grapefruit stuck anywhere it shouldn't be.

But there is some hope. Dr John Bergman in his latest video on cancer (breaking the cycle of fear and ignorance) is a must watch - from your armchair, or hammock. John is a thorough researcher, a brilliant Doctor and a kind chiropractor. He's definitely no fan of the: cut, burn and poison brigades' approach to Wellness.

Dr Véronique Desaulniers ('Doctor V' to her friends) is badged as the Breast Cancer Conqueror. She being a breast cancer thriver, nowadays. Her style is personal. She has created 'The 7 Essentials', a step by step coaching program for preventing and healing breast cancer naturally, which lasers in on the 7 Things Your Oncologist Won't Tell You. That's more than a catchy advert, it's a pretty useful start.

She calls it out as she sees it, "Cancer cannot grow in a healthy body, it's that simple".

8. Follow the money

Somebody said once 'Follow the money'
and that is what it is all about.
Murray Walker

Money is a sign of the Big Beast, whose constant chasing devours most of us. Yes, it is a predator. Originally, money existed in scribed tablet form, then coins, then paper and now it's digital; perhaps, as its value falls, the ink-stained paper is just too expensive to print. Money has been a medium of exchange, and a store of wealth, for thousands of years. It has been shells, beads, precious metals, grains, gem stones, hides, animals and, in modern slave times, people.

To get more money people work in: jobs they hate, to afford stuff they don't need, to impress people they don't like. While commuting distances their health can barely tolerate. I was once a four hours a day London commuter, wisely learning from my Father - who commuted a mere five hours a day, for 17 years. I'm not sure what I did with all my spare time. Ah, the modern life.

Perhaps we've been chasing the wrong rainbow; all the ones I've seen have never had a pot of gold at the end of them. But in chasing financial rainbows I've met a few pirates along the way - "Arrggh, so I have, me hearties!". Especially pouring out of rush hour trains into the City of London. (In reality, a separate Country, a City State - that even the queen can't enter, uninvited). So, money really does have power.

Initially, we willingly give any amount of time to make and save money. But as we age, we'd pay any amount of money to get back time. Health too, if we think about it. Money symbolises the burning of the creative energy of people, willing to sacrifice a portion of their lifetime for something they deem more valuable - a shiny Merc perhaps. At the time. When we're young, we think we have lots of time - that we'll live forever and are healthily immortal. At the latter stages - if we've not died young - we'll be paying someone a Kings' ransom to wipe our backside and feed us our baby food dinner at 4pm. And later, to change our nappy if we can't. For too long, I've chased more money.

So, where do Countries (and City States) spend this money - derived from the creative energy of the masses, crammed cheek by jowl on the 7.15 into London Bridge? Well, they spend it mainly on sick, that's what. On both sides of The Pond.

The US tops the chart on sick spend with, a wallet busting, 18% of GDP (Gross Domestic Product) on their health care industry. Of those three words only industry is accurate. Perhaps, in our distraction, GDP is really Grossly Distracted Priorities. If we look with fresh eyes (and changed bed pans) we'd see that the industry is a machine of massive meat grinding proportions. Too harsh? Well, the simplest evidence is in plain sight.

The US spends 20x more per patient than Cuba ($10,000 per patient per annum versus a measly $500) but is sicker on literally every measure. So how is that? Well, with no dog in this fight, some say it's to do with: less false positives of over diagnoses, a much reduced vaccine schedule and far fewer invasive 'treatment' operations. Plus, maybe, the Cubans have a more direct line in conversations, 'It's yer diet doing for your digestive tract, baby' and less sharp tongued chit-chat, such as, 'we can whip out yer gallbladder (and drain yer bulging wallet at the same time) Mr Money Machine'.

The UK is following along too, on spending more to be less well. In the UK, of which the Isle of Man is actually (despite denials) a part, the official National Health spending is £162 billion. That's £162,000,000,000 in old money - and only £70 billion more than expended on education. A bargain. If paying for more diseased folks is an accountants measure of value.

Meanwhile, at the lower end of spend, almost all medics enter the profession to help others, engulfed for years in learning and college fees. Studying late into the night with countless 50p's going into the meter. But if we trip across to the US, let's see if those late nights are worth it, simply on a financial, cash-ectomy basis. In August 2017, it was: orthopaedic surgeons earning $450k, cardiologists $382k, radiologists $374k, plastic surgeons $350k, anaesthetists $ 350k, emergency surgeons $314k (to be blunt, if I had a sharp telegraph pole sticking out of my intestines, I'd pay the emergency surgeon a bit more to stop carving the Thanks Giving Day turkey and rush to my roadside accident). Meanwhile, Ophthalmologists get a less than eye watering $250k.

Back at med school, doctors advancing upwards try, as they do, to comprehend the complexity of the human body. A body in which each different cell knows every other, communicating moment to moment, awake or asleep, from head to toe. When to birth, to breath, to grow, and with programmed cell death, when to die. Before long, though, the gaze is redirected within a health system focused on prescriptions, fixed protocols and pricing. Fixed pricing. The seven billion variables, sometimes known as people, stealthily becoming a commercial cost centre. Whether the medics see it or not. In the brave new world of red ink 'health', the pen really is mightier than the stethoscope.

When Dr Sherri Tenpenny presented on the Isle of Man on the 3rd and 4th December 2018, she said in her filmed presentation that, "Healthy people are not good for business and that the business model of the vaccine industry is to make people perpetually sick".

That was a: whoa, hold your horses Calamity Jane, moment. I even had a management type individual button hole me later on and verbally spank me. Yet, the more we look into the rabbit hole, the clearer we see their business model. But distraction is easier to stomach, if the horse has unseated the jockey.

Might we dot join, to see if there might be a financial connection to more, or even excessive, medical activity. We'd possibly start with Merck, the manufacturers of Gardasil, the HPV vaccine, who are opening a new (600 job...) Gardasil plant in Ireland. Also, they are now opening fertility clinics...

I've loosely connected the two activities, as Gardasil contains Polysorbate 80, patented to cause infertility in dogs. That Gardasil is causing worldwide premature ovarian failure in young women could sustain a valuable new business model. With decade long falling fertility the average cost of each Merck fertility cycle is $10,000 - $15,000. With Gardasil costing less than $4 per dose to make, yet retailing at $150 per dose, the cynical amongst us might wonder if there is an upstream connection.

Alongside, it's certainly big business, even when the vaccine is free to the end patient. With Quarter 1 sales in 2019 of $532 million, the Gardasil HPV vaccine generates $2 billion in annual sales. Sales which have grown 40% since 2018. But, perhaps, this dash for cash has blinded some?

Although he has been dead for 51 years Upton Sinclair had it well nailed, "It is difficult to get a man (or woman) to understand something, when his salary depends upon his not understanding it".

The 'health' industry certainly works to a decades long plan, and so should you. It doesn't get to be a $ multi-trillion industry without knowing where it is heading, and ensuring that it gets there. That's why in US non election years, 70% of funding of some TV stations comes from the pharmaceutical industry. Such free spending, and market seeding, has been going on for decades. Without a press fanfare - fuelling over the counter yet under the radar spending.

In the 1970's Henry Gadsden, the boss of Merck Pharmaceuticals wanted, he said, to make medical drug taking as everyday, "commonplace as chewing gum". He might have intoned us to breath fresh air instead, as some notice that gum gets stuck in the throat and gut. He certainly achieved his business aims; under his tenure, from 1965 to 1975, Merck's turnover quadrupled. He died in 1980, aged 69, but his legacy lives on.

Money and mis-health are all 'anecdotal' and a 'coincidence' after all. In examining Merck's Vioxx - an arthritis 'wonder drug' - which underwent clinical scrutiny followed by FDA approval in 1999, it was allegedly 'proven' to be 'safe and effective'. Subsequently prescribed to 80 million people it was belatedly withdrawn from the market after 100,000 deaths. Of the $5 billion fine, $321 million was for criminal activities. A mere drop in the ocean of sales. That Merck coincidentally makes Gardasil, their HPV vaccine, encourages some to use the HPV moniker, 'Helps Pay for Vioxx'.

In the US, National Public Radio had a sad case recently of a hospital nurse with cancer who, despite private insurance, was struggling with her bills. Through all the testing, chemo, blood draws and scans, it was not actually the treatment that got this patient down, but the complexity of the medical billing system. More than 40% of the 9.5 million US citizens diagnosed with cancer, from 2000 to 2012, spent their life savings within two years. A cancer diagnosis is highly 'profitable'. Walking out of the door well - is perhaps less so.

They say if a job's worth doing, do it well. Or, if in Spain, 'put it off until tomorrow'. If you enter the medical profession you know three things: it will be long hours, hard work and, with luck, rewarding. But the reality sees doctors burning out with increasing frequency, suiciding at rates higher than the public at large, and having greater addiction problems. The money, six figures of salary in pounds or dollars, clearly isn't enough. Each week a new inspection, a new compliance issue or a new protocol.

It's not just the medics who get a slice of the pie; others, feeling they were underfunded over 50 years ago, included lab tethered and tenured scientists. In 1967, Harvard Scientists no less, were paid to slant the research finding to demonise fats. Not sugar. In the intervening 50 years, hundreds of millions of people have been defrauded by fake statins science, and their lives lived healthily, cut short. As statins is now a $100 billion industry turning that expensive supertanker round can't happen soon enough.

QOF That Champers Old Chap - We've Blown £30 billion On An Un-Healthy Experiment.

Dictionary meaning of quaffing: 'to drink a lot in a short time'. But this Quaff or more precisely QOF, refers to the UK's Governmental: Quality Outcomes Framework. The name alone says for sure: you've been, oh, so simply quangoed. My distracted munchkins.

In 2018, a mindful management type individual emailed me the QOF(fing) article which, of course, doubled my inbox. The subject line was headed: One For You. Ominous words those, so I opened it gingerly... Perhaps a time limited manhood extension or that my long lost Dictator relatives have 30 million large ones to deposit into my bank account - pronto. But I was wrong. Management man was making a sound point, pointing his pointy digit at waste in government spending. No, just like you - I thought - surely not?

The article was penned by Jerome Burne and great it was, outlining what he called the biggest health experiment ever. Conducted in Britain, the trial ran for 15 years and cost - in round numbers - £30 billion. Nine noughts were not the big problem, unless they have a 30 at the front of them. Plus a pound sign. But following such big ticket largess, there has been barely a squeak; not even a public whisper about what was achieved. Or not.

The QOF study focus was on: heart disease, cancer, and a composite of all non-targeted conditions. Mr Burne's article highlighted: the largest ever 'health' trial which tested the effectiveness and safety of using drugs to cut the risk of developing chronic disease. It was astonishing and revealed a massive failure of a major plank in public health policy. Yet these findings have remained effectively secret. Aimed and Shamed. The trial aimed to save 10,000 lives, cut hospital admissions and increase life expectancy. All very laudable.

Yet, it did none of those - 'natch' of course, obviously. I say 'obviously' because the first 'stat' being a biggish round number confirmed that it was a guess. Four noughts tell you nought, even if they have a 1, 2, 3, or 10 in front of them. The trial was likely baked, as in cooked up, by right thinking and left leaning Committeeistas looking for: near term whole cycle metrics of diversity to aid inclusive moral agendas of sustainable healthcare fit for purpose in the 21st Century under a changing climate of white privilege. Or some such.

Back to the QOF trial as published in the Lancet in May 2016: long-term Evidence for the Effect of Pay For Performance in Primary Care on mortality in the UK: a population study by: AM Ryan, S Krinsky, E Kontopantelis, and T Doran. They studied all cause (precise, hard to deny, binary) mortality between 1994 and 2010. They stated: "the QOF was not associated with significant changes in mortality. Our findings have implications for the probable effects of similar programmes on populations health outcomes". Ooops, Matron. All at a cost of £30 billion - hardly a free bursary recommendation for getting Einstein into Oxford is it? The ball was not so much dropped as punctured and eaten by a strong jawed staffie, in the local park. Hide that amongst fake news, Harry.

To be fair (for once) it wasn't actually a trial; there were no 'control' subjects. It couldn't have had a control group because the guinea pigistas were the entire UK population. You be the judge of what could possibly go wrong statistically speaking. In fact, only you should be the judge of such a 'no controls' trial - one done to you and with your money. Less an out of body, more an out of wallet, experience. Repeat after me, "Doc, can you medicate your way to Wellness?" - although you can masticate yourself to it. Or not. Example A: when Delia Berry Whittingstall knocks up a cake you can be sure it needs two eggs - for that perfect Victoria Beckham Sponge. One that Granny won't have to take her teeth out to enjoy - nor the ever smiling queen Victoria.

Just add two eggs, no more no less - unless egg on FaceTime beckons. But in the case of government slow cooked books, you know - just know - to follow the dough. Always. Likely, such burnt offerings will be quickly forgotten and buried around the time of the next election. With the QOF project we may just have started a 'disease-mongering' model - one from which it's increasingly hard to escape.

However, with this continual 'health' focus, it doesn't seem to make us less frequent visitors to the sick bay. Looking at the NHS, their UOBNED (Upwards Only But Never Enough Dosh) spend, we're not just running out of acronyms - we're also running out of well people. What if we become so sick that there were no 'worried well' customers left in daily circulation? What if, finally, there is no one healthy to work in hospitals? If you become the last well person in Britain please

130

turn the lights out!

Being a bit more objective and evidence based it's clear the UK's belt, buckles and budgets have expanded directly in 'sync' - or should that be: in sink and fridge, along with our over-stocked freezers. With all the billions of new spend, of bells and whistles, of daily talk of 'breakthrough' drugs are coming it is certain that we're not 'beating cancer' any time soon.

Talking of bells and whistles, just where is the NHS Court Jester when you really need one? It's toe curling to see that QOF actually added less than nothing, except a £30 billion hole painted in red ink on national finances. Meanwhile, we have enslaved 50 something men and women on their needless 'protocol' pills. De-prescribing treatment is always the hardest pill to swallow. Mr Burne does well to highlight these unhealthy goings on while Rome smoulders. Clearly this Jerome is not fiddling - but many others very well might be.

Fill Yer BOOTS On The NHS - Guilty As (Over) Charged.

Jumping jack flash, hold the front page. Shock and horror. The headline of 2nd February 2018: 'Times INVESTIGATION' (in capitals, so we know we SHOULD shouty, shouty, and with lips a pouty pay attention!). The lead story confirmed that they've rifled through digital waste bins and old paper invoices to get evidence of the NHS playing fast (and especially very loose) with 'our' cash. It seems they have been coughing up the odd £1,500 for a £2 pot of moisturiser. Unbelievably odd, in fact. Quite. I nearly coughed and choked on that, too. But, for context, with a £162 billion NHS budget, blowing a measly fifteen hundred quid seems barely a pimple on the NHS's backside. Or a rat's arse. More than a healthy 'tip' too, that £1,498 mark up on a £2 item. Presumably, 'said' moisturiser was accompanied by an eight grand jar of smelling salts for Matron. Maybe we are into peak 'buy one get one free' season - we need to know, and pretty soon.

Morgan, Stanley? Well, 'no other car would do' - The Journo who penned the article really had me: leaned in, turned on and tuned in to his words. He's clearly a splendid Wordsmith and Writerist, is Paul Morgan-Bentley. Any fella named after two of Britain's finest examples of hand-crafted, top pimped metal - well, he would be worth reading, wouldn't he? At least the article finally gave me a clue as to what I was about to uncover, all in depth and at source - it being listed under the 'Health' and 'NHS' categories rather than under 'expensive champagne' and 'corked' headings. Those titles often being interchangeable.

Coconut Water(gate) - So, tricky Dicky, "I am not a crook", please help me lift the lid on all of this, if you would. The next overcharged item is none other than that nectar of the Gods: virgin, 'luxurious' oil of coconut. This glassed up gem has been changing hands for just 650 of those splendidly quaintly old, and empire building, British pounds. Nay palm was greased - 'but at least you got a free lid, Dicky'. There it was, front of page and front of centre: CoconutGate 'jar photo' in all of its two tone glory. But, actually, we didn't need a photo; coconuts are pretty easy for us to picture especially those of us who still have a brown and white telly. Photography, it's nuts!

It seems Boots, allegedly - or their associates - filled their not so much boots as their shiny, upsold, calf length Louboutin's. If such prices are what High Street Chemists currently charge then likely they're playing Monopoly - but now their High Street is Park Lane and Mayfair all rolled into one. With Hotels on them.

Meanwhile, someone's Grannie is lying on a trolley waiting for a new hip, with scarcely a bottle (or jéroboam) of Chateau Laffite '69 anywhere to be found. For 12 hours. Especially not amongst Nurse Nellie, on her latest extended hours shift labouring under the latest management 'power saving' lights wheeze. One clearly set to: extra dim. There's money - but not

132

going where we think it should, Jim.

'Specials' are those medical items that are ordered at short notice, requiring specialist attention and care, to ensure that their bespoke nature doesn't compromise their safety nor their quality. In fact, just like that personally bespoke Morgan or Bentley car, you should expect to pay extra for that panel crafted, hand polished, masterpiece.

But rogue pharmacists and suppliers beware. There is increasing regulation and greater scrutiny to identify any wrong 'uns amongst the NHS. Especially those running a couple of latest spec' Lear Jets on the proceeds from a 'lock up' shop (open three days a month, between 12 noon and 3pm) but closed on Saturdays. Suppliers selling three small jars of aspirin once a year to the NHS.

All this goes to show that, as with anything in life, we should always read the small print. A simple solution to all this? Well, one quite simply that would require all NHS suppliers to highlight their terms in bold and red, stating clearly: this product may contain buts. And ifs.

Sadly, Winter is The Season of mass sickness - from a few sniffles, to plenty of colds, through to full blown worldwide flu epidemics. More tragically, is to read of hospitals where people have died whilst parked up in the corridors, before even getting into a spare bed on the ward. The natural reaction everywhere is, that 'health' budgets are too small with every type of treatment 'under funded'.

The 'above inflation rate' spending increases of the last thirty years have somehow not been nearly enough. But what IF the model is, dare we say, wrong? The invoice for which someone else is paying. Increasingly, with no accountability.

What if, by calling sick treatment 'health', we don't just delude the patients and staff but the ever more pressured crowdfunding taxpayers who are asked to dig deeper too?

What if we defined Wellness and renamed the NHS the NSCS? The National Sick Care Service. Care being the vital word and being lawfully (not legally) enshrined as a duty on a journey towards long-term patient Wellness.

What if a 'see at a glance' measurement of immune system resilience could be measured, maintained or even improved, right into old age? What if the lessons of wholesale, multi decade, antibiotic resistance were learnt and a less IS more philosophy was adopted? It's cheaper too long-term. What if the causes of inflammatory diseases were heeded and a 'social contract' binding all governments to not make them worse by their actions? "Nurse, please unplug the carbonated drinks and denatured food machine" as a simple starter. The Hospital is the most expensive 'hotel' in which any off us will dwell.

"Nurse, pass me the scalpel - finally it's time for that Radicalectomy". We need new thinking that cuts deep into the 'spend more yet we get worse' mentality. What about incrementally taking up to 20% of the budget and applying it to defined 20 year Wellness goals? Or, perhaps, starting a true Wellness Fund with the sole goal of keeping people Well - and rewarding 'the system workers' accordingly. Only then can we start to build an Informed Patient Physician Partnership for the next generation - and as an essential part of our educational curriculum. That way we won't use up all their health 'green shield stamps', nor overplay the 'get out of jail free' cards of youth. If we never bite the informed patient bullet we'll be burdened by society's hand brake with an upwards only, 'health' spend - yet on increasingly sick people.

I'd forgotten that the money in keeping people healthily sick has been diverted for quite a while. More in the renewal subscription model than in the one off payment to an undertaker. This is taken from a leaflet I'd written nearly 20 years ago, entitled: 'Charity Watch'. I used to hand it out to tin rattlers.

The facts....how 'charities' spend some of their income (Figures are taken from their 2000/2001 accounts).

Charity	Highest paid director (& staff details)
Age Concern	Up to £90,000, for EACH of 3 Directors
Barnardo's	Up to £89,999 each, also 4 staff £60,000 +
British Heart Foundation	Up to £120,000 also 2 others @ £100,000 +
Cancer Research Campaign	Up to £100,000 also 22 people @ £40,000 +
Help the Aged	Up to £89,999 also 8 @ £50,000 plus
NSPCC	Up to £100,000 each, for 2 Directors
OXFAM	£40,000 10 staff, (only 6 @ £40,000 in '99)
People's Dispensary for Sick Animals	Up to £70,000 2 staff, and 5 @ £50,000 +
RNIB	Up to £90,000 also 6 above £50,000
Royal National Lifeboat Institution	Up to £79,999 also 1 above £60,000
Royal Soc' for the Protection of Birds	Up to £80,000 also 12 above £40,000

Save the Children	Up to £80,000 also 13 above £40,000
Scope	At least £80,001, exact figure not given
WWF - UK	Up to £80,000 also 5 staff above £50,000

Charities rarely announce the above salaries when they are running their fund raising campaigns. Playing on emotional appeal, they 'sell' an image of charity but pay as a fat cat 'business'. The accounts show low admin figures, but salaries are shown elsewhere, often masking the real costs of their 'business'. All legal, though carefully 'presented'.

Figures from 2003 Annual Report & Accounts show Barnardo's staff have done very well since 2001. The Chief Executive now earns up to £109,999, one person earns up to £89,999, 3 are paid up to £79,999, 11 are paid up to £69,999, and 13 paid up to £59,999.

Many Chief Executives have final salary pension schemes, so will receive over £1million during retirement from their former 'charity' employer. That needs to be paid BEFORE the needy get anything. Huge built in liabilities before the GIVING begins. Then add in the computers, heating, the £1 million TV begging campaigns and fancy London offices. Why don't they mention that in their adverts?

Charity shops often rely on the goodwill of volunteers, gaining well intentioned help locally. This though, is subsidised by local tax and rate payers and so distorts local commerce.

What should I do with this information?
1) Ignore it, as we all need to make a living! Gimme that gravy train baby!

2) Accept it as the price of cleansing my conscience when I give to charity.
3) Think before I give in future. Should I give to those without FANCY head offices?
4) Cut out the fat cats and give directly to small, local, low cost, front line charities.

Meanwhile, back in the US (the home of good health…) the price of insulin has been rising for a Century. Some diabetics even use crowdfunding pages to raise money for their medicine. People are spending as much on insulin as on mortgage payments or home rental. The issue has been raised by Senator Bernie Sanders amid class action lawsuits with accusations of collusion and price fixing. Nevada has proposed legislation to deal with the issue. In the most recent decade insulin prices have risen 300%; however, that's just following an upwards only insulin pricing trend. Eli Lilly and Novo Nordisk raised their prices again in 2017 to keep each other company. Coincidence being easier to spell than collusion.

Humalog (known as Lispro, made by Eli Lilly) and NovoLog (made by Novo Nordisk) are the two major insulin 'products' which have risen from $25 per bottle in 1996 to $275 by 2016. Better than making cars or building houses - margin wise - some may say. In normal markets prices tend to fall through scales of economy as volumes increase. But, remarkably over 20 years, during a time when diabetes hasn't exactly been on a downwards trajectory, prices haven't fallen; they've escalated in a 'gold taps for the Maldives condo, Larry' type way.

Near the top of the festering money pile, let's start with the $multi-billion, US National Vaccine Injury Compensation Program. Yes, Nurse, there is one - although that was unknown to a leading Manx GP, until we had lunch on the 3rd December 2018 when I informed him. It has only been in existence since 1986 so he may have been distracted back then by the miners' strike, and in the next 34 years by Strictly Come Celebrity Bake

Off On Ice In The Jungle.

The US NVIC fund has paid out a total of over $4.271 billion to date. This is the money paid out behind closed doors having been heard by 'special masters' until January 2020. Some 92% of that ($3.934 billion) has been compensation to Petitioners. Despite only 1 in 100 harms being reported (see the Harvard Pilgrim study) and far, far, fewer of those cases making it to trial. Even then, there have only ever been 7014 compensation awards made; another 5487 cases ended up being dismissed.

Of course, the 8% balance of money paid by the Program (some $336.79 million) being the fees to Attorneys representing all the claimants - whether compensated or dismissed. The lawyers always get paid their $$$.

The UK being more miserly, limits vaccine injury pay-outs to £120,000 each. But why should all this be kept secret, when (hack alert) Anonymous are increasingly ready at the door, laptop and smart phone in hand? In the US the number 1 cause of bankrupted people are their: medical bills.

On every measure, in the last forty years, chronic treatment spending has far out-paced acute accident spend. Chronic is the new emergency - it is going to bankrupt the world.

More locally, the Isle of Man has just had a review. Yes, another one. Mirroring more spend on everything with no increase in quality of life, nor pill-free health, length of life. Yes, length still matters. The Island now aims to spend £7,500 / person by 2035 on being sick. Let's drink to that.

It has a Public Health budget less than 1% of total 'sick' spend. So more than 99% goes on treating sick people and they've not all been hit by a truck nor got their finger caught in a mangle.

As 'the only thing constant is change', as of January 2020, the man from the ministry in charge of the Manx sick service has just got an extra £8 million of financial taxpayer funded largesse added to his bloated budget. We should be well by the morning.

A generation ago Tammy Wynette 'sang': 'No Charge'. Since then we have morphed into a dystopian 'sick as health model' world. One where hospital visitors are 'customers' is the new mantra. So, while you're making that Florence Nightingalesque 'dusk dash' to get Grannie her clean knickers - Mr Huxley lurks, clipboard in hand, behind his £10 per minute parking barrier. Less 'stand and deliver' and more 'crawl and be thankful'. Welcome to a brave new world of the NHS.

Meanwhile, fighting the upwards only spend trend, I see that Vermont (in the US) and China (not 5G test-bed Wuhan) have some 'pay for Wellness' schemes but almost no one else does. Haven't they been handed the script by Dean Koontz?

What are they smoking - and just what are those guy$$$ thinking?

Don't laugh at me 'cause I'm a fool; so sang Norman Wisdom in the film, 'Trouble in Store', released nearly 70 years ago in 1953. I first saw the film in black and white when I was about six years old, give or take. Over four decades later I moved, unintentionally, to where Norman had also made his home. To his, and my, beloved Isle of Man nestling in the middle of the Irish Sea. The title of his song hit me then and now, a few decades later, as it also rings a bell. It tolls for me does tune and time. Regularly smacking me round the head with all the deft precision of a well wielded cricket bat. Wake up, fool!

So, here goes oh shallow one...

Today, while scrolling through my phone notes, I see that five years ago, on 29th January 2015, I was at a meeting in Noble's Hospital. That was at a time when I was deep in my brown tongue poopy - sorry, puppy - dog, phase. I was there to help launch a bowel screening app, to promote earlier screening; an idea clean round the bend, I'd later reckon. As, the more I've looked at illness screening programmes around the world, the more they appear to find cancers that aren't real, often aren't life threatening nor urgent, yet give birth to a new 'life' of mental and physical anguish. Accompanied by the 'kerching' of the cash register. In the case of bowel screening, it seems to me, based on sh!t screening, Matron.

As we know, it's not just the proctologist who likes to keep his hand in - just I was being piped aboard the good ship: HMS Re-Sectioner. I'd become a half asleep aider and abetter, an Orwellian styled: Useful Idiot. But please don't laugh at me because I was a different kind of fool, then.

Going back nearly two decades, in 2001, I had some spare money. Having had a 25 bagger (turning £8,000 into £200,000 is a heady feeling) as I'd backed Nettec, an internet start up, that was hot to trot and newly floated on AIM (Alternative Investment Market). The aim being that we all get stinking rich, along with latter day and lazy, Loads-a-Money types. Pop yer corks boys & girls.

So, with that much wonga burning a hole in my pocket (and some might say to defer capital gains tax, M'Lud) I put £50k down on the craps table of life. Or, more precisely as judy might read this, I'd studiously backed a University spin-out company. It was to be another roll of the financial dice. Or, the plural die might actually have been more appropriate, being that it was a chemo company. Backing Oncoprobe with £50,000 was in a period, to quote my much ignored (but later right) Wife 'when I thought I was Rothschild'. But wasn't. The £50,000 I lost validates the saying, 'If you think knowledge is expensive, try ignorance'. Topped off with, 'you pleb'. The other 'co-investors' lost over £1 million - and that over 13 slow, car crash, up and down the motorways, eventful years. With a fair bit of door slamming to boot. But losing the money was not my major crime…. What wasn't I thinking, to go and back a: bespoke chemo 'therapy' company? A bit like stumping up for: napalm light, or diet mercury or friendly fire. In all cases, death is usually the reality check result. That the bespoke chemo relied on a cell signature which minutely and accurately married, some claimed, to tell which kind of chemo your cells most appreciate. Rather than those cells of fat Billy, from down the pub. Apparently we're all a bit different - he likes lager while you like mild and bitter and crisps. Our cells are like that too - they've different tastes.

Oncoprobe ebbed and flowed for over a decade with new funders, partners, channel sales lines and regulatory discussions; but little real world, Nature taming, solutions. If I'd heard that, 'Nature always bats last' way back in 2001, I might just have avoided beaching 50,000 quaint British pound notes up on the sandbanks of life. More likely, I wouldn't have as I was reading the same regurgitated stuff as everyone else. Hook, line and stinker.

Maybe, if someone had jabbed me in both eyes with a javelin, while muttering you'd best watch: 'Why the majority is always wrong' by Paul Rulkens, on TED, I may just have listened - while wiping the blood from both eyes. Somehow I doubt it, as I really wasn't ready and that's the long and short of it. Sadly, that TED video didn't air until 2014 so I was more than on my own. The stumbling is all part of the race, apparently.

What better than to recall, 'when the student is ready the teacher appears'. So what if life is actually unfolding just as it should? Perhaps, I am just the fool I'm meant to be - right now.

9. Informed consent

A man is usually more careful of his money than of his principles.
Oliver Wendell Holmes, Jr.

It's strange how words change over time; from the Middle Ages of ye olde English fast forward to modern street l'argot of down wiv da hood, yo, bro. So words matter, at the right time, in the right place, if we're to be understood or buy something 'interesting' on a street corner from an agent of one of the Alphabet Soup agencies (like the CIA or FBI). There are two words to which we give special attention and that is: our rights. It's said 'if we don't know our rights then we have none'. If we can weigh up a decision based on true facts so much the better. But it seems the table is skewed; the odds are fixed and the house, not the punter, tends to win. Trickier still is when the winning bet is about to fall into our lap and someone jogs the table or spills his hot cocoa on the baize.

Inflationary language is rampant amongst the disease-mongering community. In fact, it is in all industries. In double glazing speak it is called upselling. Mrs Slocombe phones up to buy a cat flap for her pussy and by the end of the evening her whole house has been double glazed. Similarly, in the medical business, a doctor behind with some payments on his ski lodge (and his mistress) might not always insist you read all the small print. Twice, in a good light. So caveat emptor should be foremost in our minds - when it's his scalpel versus your wallet. Think rock, paper, scissors on steroids.

All patients should ask to see the PIL (Patient Information Leaflet) and then study carefully its contents where it lists the possible harms and stated ingredients. There's a bit of coded language there too, so that the Mums and Dads (and doctors) don't realise the utter toxic and unpronounceable products being swallowed by, or injected into, their beloved. Likely, not one in ten reading this book would ask to see a PIL and, if they did, would not know the odds ratio of risks versus benefit of their treatment. More likely still, they could quote the ingredients (and cooking time) of a tasty tiramisu but don't know whether chemo (or low-fat napalm) works best on their five year old. It's how we've been educated - but if I was going to France and my life depended on it, I wouldn't start from here, as some wit once said. A shining wit no doubt.

The role of US paediatricians is focused on small adults, little patients, a special breed of customer on whom they earn a major part of their income from vaccines. We know finance could never, ever, sway the mind of any man (or woman) but I mention it, just as a back stop - in case anyone in the cheap seats was wondering. In most cases if a paediatrician doesn't dish up big dollops of vaccines their practice would not be viable. No 'well visits' would be required.

Perhaps there is an organisation called PAID (Paediatricians Against Informed Decisions)? If 63% of a practice is fully vaccinated, according to schedule, the paediatrician receives $400 / patient. With a practice of 1,000 patients that's $400,000 income. Could that sway anyone to not always provide informed decision making? I doubt it, too, but let's peer behind the screens just to be sure.

The medical industry remains broadly immune to any criticism, 'my patient may not have liked dying but at least her hair does look good in the coffin'. Some have a reputation for not knowing the difference between God and a Surgeon? God doesn't know he's God. Or She, obviously.

So what is an ultimate upsell? Well a DCIS (Duct Carcinoma In Situ) 'cancer' for one. The ethical guys say it shouldn't be called a carcinoma, or cancer, at all. It's not just the doctors who may need better training - we the patients need to ask some probing questions. To dig just a bit more before writing out our Saturday morning list - the Walkers crisps will still be on offer next week with luck.

Most of all we need to focus on the words of a young Manx doctor who said of her profession, "we are all just disease-mongers". Such an observation and direct expression of youth might well hit the nail on the head - but stop her getting promoted. So, are we complying with informed consent laws? It's dubious at best. Let's take a glance at what should protect our interests as people, not rushing headlong to become patients. Let's go beyond casual consent and make a really active choice.

The Montgomery Ruling: As published in the BMJ, 12th May 2017. The ethical and legal position is clear: doctors must not withhold information simply because they disagree with the decision the patient is likely to make if given that information.

The UNESCO (the Education, Science and Culture arm of the UN) Universal Declaration on Bioethics and Human Rights - enshrines human dignity. It states: "The interest and welfare of the individual should have priority over the sole interest of science or society". On Informed Consent it is equally clear: "Any preventive, diagnostic and therapeutic medical intervention is only to be carried out with the prior, free and informed consent of the person concerned, based on adequate information".

The Nuremberg Code - The 1940's truly were a dark period in the history of the World. A period when medical experiments on humans were at their height, or depth. When racial superiority of some reduced others to sub species, to be used and abused with less than no compassion. The outcome, as World War II ended, were the Nuremberg Trials to ensure that medical experimentation never happened again. A Code was implemented to control the ethics of experimentation and to ensure that individuals were afforded equal rights - rights aligned with the 2,500 year old Hippocratic Duty.

The Hippocratic Oath - Forbids the Administering of Poisons: "Neither will I administer a poison to anybody when asked to do so, nor will I suggest such a course". I wonder what he would have made of aluminium salts used as vaccine adjuvants - a product never tested against an inert placebo. Ever. The Hippocratic Oath of the medic calls their conscience to, "First, do no harm".

What if we went back to the future and adopted the words of Hippocrates, as the first man of medicine, "Let food be thy medicine and medicine be thy food"? What an anarchist that old geezer was. I bet he had a beard, too, and sandals fulltime - not just at weekends. And likely a dangerous rolling stone tablet collection. He also proclaimed other heresies, I believe, such as: "Don't make money in the sick room". Top man. Maybe we can make money in the Well Room?

10. Considering Common Law

There is no greater tyranny than that which is perpetrated under the shield of the law and in the name of justice.
Montesquieu

For decades I'd heard the saying that the pen is mightier than the sword, yet I had ignored it. I just thought it was a quaint saying although, if the pen was wielded by Oscar Wilde, I thought it might just be true. Then, just over 12 months ago, I realised that the pen is indeed far mightier than the sword. But with any lightbulb moment you've really got to know where you're dipping your nib - and especially who's holding the ink pot. I learnt much of this in Spain, on the fly, watching erect and upstanding lawyers at work. Or so I thought.

'It isn't that they can't see the solution, it's that they can't see the problem' opined GK Chesterton. That was me.

I'd flown to Madrid for some tapas and talking, and in five days managed to get in a fair bit of both, with a Spanish lawyer friend. As a medico-legal expert he'd authored his first book on drug harms. His latest case concerned a post menopausal drug on which he had invited me to sit in. It was to be heard in Valencia and I could spend three days in the public gallery, brushing up my Spanish and, less enjoyably, watching older ladies, taking the drug Agreal, collapse at our feet.

The legal issue centred on harms caused over long-term use. The report from Sanofi, the manufacturer, highlighted the drug should only be taken in three, short time periods. Initially, take for 20 days followed by a ten day gap, then take for another 20 days followed by a ten day gap, then take for the final 20 days. That makes 80 days total in the treatment cycle. Not the decade for which some women had been prescribed Agreal.

A major issue was that the judge dismissed the official Sanofi report which had highlighted known harms since 2007. As it was now 2019, even I figured that no one could be that slow to read any report, unless it was written in extremely small print. Or possibly, in words that the judge didn't wish to see, which were incriminating, and guilt laden, of his friends. This was unless, of course, he had another agenda and was, himself, a criminal - to be blunt.

First thing on the first day I walked quickly with my lawyer friend to get his black robes. Meanwhile something was dawning on me although I didn't yet know what it was. I was scrambling to recall Jordan Maxwell and his 'liberty not freedom' videos, which were still a bit of blur to me. By the end of the three Valencia days I'd started to wise up. Later, that week, returning to Madrid, I was slowly getting it. As each day dawned, it got better - legal and Lawful are not the same. Finally, it was wham! and: wake me up before you go, go. The black robes were legal symbols of what was going on. They really were evidence that lawyers and courts were mourning justice, in plain sight.

Back in Madrid, late one night I was walking home after dinner from Plaza Mayor and, on turning the corner, I spotted a well lit bookshop. Although it was after 11pm the shop was open. Plumb centre in the window, in pride of place, was the famously thought provoking 1984 by George Orwell. My mind flashed back to Orwell's Animal Farm, which I'd last read at school nearly 50 years before. But not in Madrid. I went inside and spent the best €11.65 of my life. Back at my hotel I didn't put the light out until 2.30am, such was the power of the words of Winston Smith, and the coming jackbooted tyranny. It echoed as disturbingly as ever, especially in January 2019. The pen was indeed mightier than the sword when George was wielding it.

Not long after, in May 2019, while attending the Autism One

148

Conference in Chicago I was honoured to have a private breakfast meeting with Bobby Kennedy. When you meet a Kennedy, it's hard not to be awestruck. Robert F. Kennedy, Jr, comes from a long line of driven social activists. His Father and Uncle spoke out about the Deep State and the Military Industrial Complex. Sadly their lives were cut short by evil men, from within their own social standing.

Bobby is now, along with Del Bigtree, focused night and day on highlighting increasing vaccine carnage. When Bobby talks of 'Uncle Jack' you know to concentrate, and hard. He confirmed he was 900 pages into a $1 trillion vaccine carnage law suit. Over the months to come, it would increasingly dawn on me that even a professional as driven as Bobby will struggle to get justice in the current legal - not Lawful - 'court' system.

Dick Turpin was a famous highwayman but at least he cried out, "Stand and deliver!". If he were alive today, and travelling, his driving licence and passport would both bear his name, if he chose to have them. They would identify his per-son. But only in a strict, defined format, as dictated by others.

Here's a quick and simple test - see IF your driving licence has your NAME in ALL CAPITALS on it. If it has, then you have been CORPORATISED. A driver is what they call a 'legal fiction', a paper person, a strawman. Or more simply an invention. Dick Turpin was a traveller on horseback; that was his conveyance of choice. But now, by becoming an all capitals DRIVER of a vehicle - and by 'conveying' in a vehicle you have unwittingly signed up to commerce. Because a vehicle is defined, unknown to you, as an object of profit engaged in commercial activity.

If we don't know our rights we have none. If you go to court (a corporate place of business) you are asked immediately for your name. They even presume to know who you are and will ask you as such: MR HEADING? A correct reply to that would be: "I was named by my parents and that name did not include

MR nor a SURNAME". However, if I reply "Yes", guess what I have then agreed to re-present? A 'legal fiction', that's what.

A man cannot be acted upon by statutes, those only apply to the fictional entity, with legal personality i.e. MR Courtenay Heading / MR C Heading.

Basically, at birth (or 'berthing' under maritime law) there are two versions of you. The living proper man / woman, but also a fictitious id-entity - a 'strawman' - created with a similar 'name' to yours. Notice how your documents appear and how your name is writ-ten. There are two types of courts - one you see and one you don't. You are no longer a free living man (or woman) but have been created, under maritime law, as a parallel entity, the 'strawman'. As it's done at 'birth', you are no longer a free man or free woman.

Our birth certificate should really be berth certificate as it marks an event; but with our name spell-ed in CAPITALS, when regis-tered, it transfers our real living being to another. Lesson one is to observe the use of the birthing certificate for most all of life processes; however, note as an exception why it cannot be used as proof of 'ID-entity'. As in 'the id', not: I.D. Ask, too, who has the original certificate and why? Trade. That's why. It's only business.

What is Common Law and how might it help nowadays, portrayed as it has been as something old and past the legal sell by date? Remember: he who creates, owns. You might wonder where finance words came from, such as: bank, cash flow - admiralty law, that's where. But you have been left 'all at sea' as to your rights and Lawful benefits.

To get at your finances when you go to the bank to draw out your money, you will note that your name is also in CAPITALS. These names have come from maritime law; on the way we have all been not just corporatised, but piratised. The

150

CAPITALS appear in plain sight: it's just that we don't see them. Or more likely we don't hear them.

We've heard the terms, Common Law Wife and Common Law Husband. It seems to have certain rights, but what if those ancient unalienable rights were what really, really, really originally protected us? All individuals were born free, and equal in dignity and rights on Earth, and no one can take that away from each of us.

What is a person? When you were born your mother / father would have submitted an application form and your per-son was created when your birth certificate was regis-tered and is evidenced by a copy of this birth certificate. REGIS = king (or queen) and you were 'g.i.f.t-dead' by your parents (handily called Informants) on the certificate to the king (or queen).

When you 'sub-mit' a regis-tration application, you are bending over to the will of another. When you register you are handing full legal title to that other. When you apply (defined as: to beg) the pre-sumption is made you know exactly what you are begging for, from whom, and what preciseley you are willing to give up for it - 'honour' amongst thieves, and all that.

In the formulation of any limited company / corporation there is always a certificate of registration to create its legal person-ality. Your fictional person known by MR, MISS, MRS or MS YOUR NAME - or Mr, Miss, Mrs or Ms Your Name - is created by the same means. Someone else is trading with, and owns, your original certificate.

Man created government which in turn created legal persons. Your person is not you, it is a legal fiction with which you are falsely identifying. You are the three dimensional living man or woman while your legal fiction is the two dimensional paper. This fictional entity is subject to civil policy jurisdiction, must fulfil all duties given to it, governed by corporate policy, such as perpetual taxes levied only under statute. Only the paper person does business in the public, controlled by civil law & corporate courts.

The remedy is to list yourself as a living being, and to take ownership of your legal fiction, via the Common Law Court. We must return to our true authority in which, as a living man or woman, we sit just below the Creator (however we each call it according to our beliefs). In that way we re-claim our Unalienable rights.

A language can only be created and used by a society; a corporation can be such a society. Legal-ese is a foreign language - the language of corporate employees. It is English but some words have very different meanings... legalese is the language of the law society. Example: Must is synonymous with may; Summons is synonymous with invitation; Understand is synonymous with stand under...

Let's first look at some of these legalese definitions:

Statutory: as created, defined or relating to a statute; required by statute; conforming to a statute.

Instrument: written legal document such as a contract, lease, deed, will or bond.

Society: the socially dominant members of a community, a society is a number of persons united together by mutual consent, in order to deliberate, determine, and act jointly for some... Common Purpose.

Contract: an agreement between two or more persons that creates or modifies an existing relationship. Offer, consideration and acceptance must exist for a contract to be made.

Constitution: The fundamental rules, written or unwritten, that establishes a character of a government by defining the basic principles to which a society must conform.

Statute: a legislative rule of society given the force of law by the consent of the governed, a rule, as of a corporation. (By its own definition it only applies to a person and not a man or woman.)

Person: includes a natural person, which is a Body Corporate. A firm, co-partnership, association, limited liability company, or corporation - all exhibit a legal personality.

It is the same in the (fake) US, with State Nations being hijacked by word sorcery. The United States is a whole different spelling as federal laws do NOT apply to a living flesh and blood American man or woman. Federal is not law. They are merely only rules, statutes and regulations - and only apply to FICTIONS (US CITIZENS). The entire US GOVERNMENT is run via a public fiction and has not run as a Republic for a long time (the lights are on, but there is no one at home). The US government hoodwinked its people into being 'transmitting utilities' (strawmen).

Anna Von Reitz knows the way home, via State Jural Assemblies, highlighting as she has the United States frauds. Continuing to play in their legal sandpits, via force of law, not rule of 'legal' statutes, simply continues the insanity. No statute has ANY power in law unless with the free CONSENT of The Governed, of: We, The People. The US is just a series of Corporations controlling the persons, the (dead) paper two dimensional entities. That's why they're Corps-orations (literally, the body-speaking).

It's no better in Canada, or as Kevin Annett and many others prefer, the Republic of Kanata. Printed on the bottom of a Canadian birth certificate are the words: Canadian Bank Note.

On a 'birth' certificate. It, and you, are treated as a financially created instrument, a bill of lading. It is not who you are. Remember, ALL CAPITAL NAMES deal only in commerce.

In New Zealand it is worth investigating information from Bill Turner (he has a channel on Youtube) .

In the UK: John Smith of Common Law Court, or John Hurst, or the late, lamented John Harris. The Brits love the name John although it was king John who had to be fully brought to book by the Barons using the Magna Carta of 1215.

In Australia look at Romley Stewart and his Justinian Deception channel (found on Youtube). He is leading the pack in his depth of understanding. As a proud Australian he says, following his seven years of research, "If it's not English it's not Common Law". Simple. But much of the legalese is complex and known as Dog-Latin. Yes, it's a barking mad language, literally. As he explains in studious detail, Romley has unpicked the complexity of Dog-Latin and it really does take the biscuit.

Income tax seems inescapable because you sign numerous documents with 'fancy' wording, stating that you are agreeing to be a representative of a corporation or entity. To get the job you have to sign the work forms. The Corporation requiring you to do so - you would lose all state benefits if it did not do so.

When your last name appears in all capitals (Capitus Diminutia Media) it means you lose your right to citizen-ship, but not to liberty. You can be fined or penalised but not enslaved nor imprisoned. But when your whole name is in all capitals it represents Capitus Diminutia Maxima (ALL CAPITAL LETTERS NAME) which states that a man's condition changes from freedom to bondage, all rights of citizenship and family rights are surrendered.

There are different kinds of 'legal law': e.g. the... Law of the Land, Martial Law, Law of Water, Admiralty Law, Maritime Law, Ecclesiastical Law, Canon Law... but we'll not look too carefully under those frocks. By design these legal law systems are extremely complex and deliberately opaque.

Those who want to control you, create a second you - and that is all denoted by CAPITAL letters. Only ALL CAPITAL LETTERS entities can be dealt with by banks and governments. If a document arrives in all capital letters you don't need to respond, as an all capital letters entity is being addressed to a parallel corporation. It just appears to be addressed to you; however, only you can give it that power, by your assumption.

The illusion is compounded, if you ever end up in 'courts' which only try the 2D paper - NEVER the living man or woman. That's why they are desperate for someone, in black robes, to represent you. As you are 'dead' to the 'court' that should really be to: re-present 'you'. You are not alive in their eyes. You don't get to say what rights and duties are, the united kingdom corporation does. When a judge in court asks you are you to confirm 'your NAME', he is asking if you wish to re-present that artificial person, the fictional 'person'. He is speaking to the you in CAPITAL LETTERS but you can't hear that. A 'court hearing' should really be called a court SPELLING.

The courts of the United Kingdom Corporation are all companies run for profit.

All UK Parliament 'Acts' are just that, an act; There is no mention of 'law' in any them. The 'rulers' know this but we don't. Yet. You do now!

If you break their rules they will 'summons' you, which is, in reality, a mere invitation. They are requesting that you visit them at their place of business to discuss your 'punishment'. If your legal fiction appears in 'court' you will get no justice. So don't play in their sandpit - it is voluntary. Such 'courts' cannot try the living man. The living man has unalienable rights to a trial by jury, requiring 12 good men or women and true, to pass a unanimous verdict of guilty or innocent. None of this matey, matey 'judge' business to let British war criminal 'leaders' off the hook.

Could the government actually take your car away and dispose of it if you actually owned it? That would be totally unlawful. They have done this on the Isle of Man to a fully Lawful, and insured, conveyance listed with Common Law Court as: CLC JURBY. The conveyance had been Lawfully de-listed from the DVLA prior to being seized by Manx Police Officers. The resolution to this matter remains ongoing at this time... under Common Law remedy.

You might be surprised to know:

The United Kingdom is a Corporation listed at: 6 Sharon Court, City of London and also with the SEC (Securities and Exchange Commission) in the US.

The House of Lords is a Corporation.

A Member of Parliament is also listed as a Corporation.

As Dun and Bradstreet confirms, 'There are 52 companies in the Isle Of Man Government corporate family.'

It's all just one big family...

The 'Isle of Man Constabulary is located in ISLE OF MAN, United Kingdom and is part of the Government Industry. Isle of Man Constabulary has 200 employees at this location.' (IM2 4RG United Kingdom).

The 'Isle Of Man Courts Of Justice... Isle Of Man Government has 3 employees at this location.' (IM1 3AR United Kingdom).

The 'Isle Of Man Prison... is part of the Government Industry. Isle Of Man Prison has 120 employees at this location.' (IM7 3JP United Kingdom).

A Police Officer (a 'legal' fiction) is a corporate revenue collector, someone employed to enforce statutes. A police constable, though, has a duty under Common Law to keep the peace, to serve and protect, and to uphold Common Law. Being a corporate enforcement officer, a police officer is not much different to the worker at Starbucks - both follow laid down company policy. While both get paid numbers at the end of each month for doing so.

Civil servants are employees of the corporation but employee status applies to every one of us too, by deception. If you have a National Insurance Number that means you too are an employee of this (country) corporation. Company policy of this corporation requiring you, as an employee, to pay tax and follow the 'policy' or 'rules' of the corporation. In doing so, you are voluntarily waiving your rights under Common Law or the US Constitution.

In stark contrast to legal laws, Common Law is simple.

Under Common Law you must cause: no harm, loss nor injury, and act with honour in all contracts.

That is (slightly) less wordy than the 2,100 pages in Black's Law Dictionary 11th Edition - on which the 'legal profession' enriches itself. At the expense of the Common Man or Woman, deceived of their rights.

Those who don't learn from history are condemned to repeat it.

Parliament swears an oath to serve the queen, but the British people do not comprehend that we the people (group noun) are sovereign; the queen manages things on our behalf. There is a contract of allegiance and she manages according to our rules and customs. Her Oath was to govern us by Common Law not statute law.

The following shows distinctions between a Natural Individual and an Artificial person:

Natural Individual	Artificial Person
Live Lawful man/woman	Dead legal personality
Lawful standing	Legal status
People make the law by the acceptance	Parliament makes statutes
The Law is the people's Common Law	Statutes are legislative instruments
We are all equal in the eyes of the Law	We're NOT all equal in the books of statutes

Laws are based on principles but statutes are based on practicalities.

Lawful trumps legal every time.

To avoid deception we must adhere to: de jure in law; not be fooled and entrapped by de facto 'in practice'.

11. Who is the criminal?

As for civil liberties, any one who is not vigilant may one day find himself living, if not in a police state, at least in a police city.
Gore Vidal

On the Isle of Man each year - on 5th July - it is tynwald day, a day of celebration of all things Manx, with visitors coming from around the world. For centuries it has been a day when Petitions of Grievance are presented to Manx politicians. It is, in that way, the ultimate theatre. In 2019, for my first attendance in years, I was wearing a yellow vest / gilets jaunes. If it's good enough as a protest sign for the French then it's good enough for me. Across the bottom of the vest in black print was 'HPV Vaccine Deaths'. On the front right hand breast was 'RIP Christina Tarsell'. On the left 'RIP Colton Berrett'. On the rear 'HPV Vaccines, Fake Trials, Real Harms'.

I'd met Emily Tarsell in the US and admired her calm manner and resolve. Her daughter Christina had died, post Gardasil vaccination in 2008, and following an eight year legal battle the vaccine court confirmed 'death by HPV vaccine Gardasil'. Colton Berrett received the HPV vaccine and his life became intolerable, resulting in his death in January 2018.

I arrived at St John's, Isle of Man at 10am, blissfully unaware that I was subsequently heading for two arrests in the next eight days. I was accompanied by three friends to witness things; two scientists and the Mum of an HPV injured daughter. On arrival I firstly paid my professional cameraman for the day - more cash for compliance than cash for questions. A couple of friends also filmed as the day unfolded which, ironically, led to them recording a beginners guide to origami of the mis-folding of my HPV vaccine Petition, undertaken on camera. By the clerk of tynwald. Having grown up reading The

Beano (comic) I fondly recall Roger the Dodger who often chanced his arm working with unsavoury characters. Although the Dodger was adept at not doing his homework and avoiding his responsibilities, this invariably led to difficulties for him down the line. Some time later. We may ultimately find, under scrutiny, that he's not such an artful dodger after all.

I recommend that you watch the video titled, 'Courtenay Heading HPV Vaccine Yellow Vest tynwald day' (https://www.youtube.com/watch?v=h_Nb2Zi3Gf0) of how the day transpired - and then tell me, in a binary manner, do you think we have free speech... yes or no?

By mid morning I arrived, under sufferance and in handcuffs, at police headquarters Douglas. As they had a limited library to pass the time, I read 'Stupid White Men' by provocative journalist Michael Moore. I'd only made it to page 44 by 2pm when the police said I was free to go 'with no charges'. I'd assumed that the 'great and the good' must have left St John's by now, and the establishment could continue to cover up the HPV vaccine crimes - hence now being lobbed a get out of jail free card, not passing go and not being slipped 200 quid either.

Having had contact with the local police, and knowing that Corvelva had lodged a criminal report with the Treviso (Italian) Police (after finding mass contaminants, missing ingredients, extra bits of unidentified origin and a banned amphetamine, APDB, in the HPV vaccine), on 7th June I also sought to obtain a Crime Number but was refused; despite one of my arresting officers, PC Cubbon, on 5th July 2019 on film, having said, "The Home Office have no jurisdiction over us, and you can have a crime number".

Monday 8th July 2019 I visited my local (Ramsey) police station - as it was their first day of business in a new week - where I met PC 114 Joyce who, coincidentally, had been an arresting sight on 5th July. He noted my request for an HPV vaccines Crime Number and said he'd look into it. Later, I had a 6pm Manx Radio interview with Dollin Mercer, as our previous chat on air had been cut short when forcibly moved on by police on 5th July. After the recording, Dollin also came outside to view my Renault Clio conveyance: CLC JURBY.

Two days later, back at Ramsey police station, I was told by PC 67 Bridges, "No you cannot have an HPV vaccine Crime Number, what you were told is incorrect - it is not something we would put on our system". Hitler didn't have a war crimes unit either, if I recall.

At lunchtime on Friday 12th July 2019, I was travelling in the Isle of Man in my lawfully (and legally) insured Renault Clio conveyance with a Common Law Court listed 'number' plate: CLC JURBY. Listing my ownership with the Common Law Court ensured that I stayed just that: the Lawful Owner. A novel concept for sure, and one which 35 million Brits (and a few Manxies) aren't - when they register their car with the DVLA (Driver Vehicle Licencing Agency). They become just the 'registered keeper'. Upon registration the king or queen of Britain becomes the legal owner. Read the not so small print - they own, you maintain.

I passed a police motorcyclist parked up beside the highway, known as Snaefell Mountain Road, noticing that he soon pulled out to follow me. About six miles further on I observed a big fella in a black costume was stood in the middle of the road with his arms up, and the blue lights on his car were flashing. I came to a halt.

Blue light man started chatting; but in a provocative way, and he seemed a little agitated. I asked him, firstly, what his problem was as he'd impeded my lawful travel. His answer seemed to me a little aggressive so, as I could see from his costume that he was a commercial officer working for a private, for profit, corporation I asked if he was, "trying to

161

contract with me".

It was easier when they were simply constables, of service, whose primary duty was to ensure the peace was kept. To, we, the people. He took a dim view and retorted, "I'm gonna get... (two ladies names) in mental health to look at you". Suddenly it was more Nutters Corner than Windy Corner.

In unrestrained (and unlawful) excitement he thrust his hands in through the open window and snatched the keys from the ignition. I gathered by his actions that I was going nowhere. The officer lacked jurisdiction, authority, and clearly hadn't done his Common Law homework; however, that did not stop him arresting me. Unlawfully.

More so, as since the 2nd July 2019, I was the named insured party for my Renault Clio, CLC JURBY, insured by Manx Cover. My number plate also bore in 10mm high letters the words 'Common Law Court' to inform others of my Lawful standing as a traveller, an unalienable right of people since the Magna Carta of 1215. Such rights existed long before DRIVER and VEHICLE were defined as (in all capital letters) legal fictions - while the designation of 'vehicle' is applicable only to commercial property.

After my unlawful arrest I was taken to police headquarters in Douglas, again. The admission sergeant this time was new to me but was busy trying to get me to 'contract'. I was staying almost entirely mute, as I knew he lacked jurisdiction and authority. He tapped my Common Law card bearing, as it does, the red cross of St George, the English flag, of the country in which I was born. He continued, "You're in the wrong place for this". I said nothing, knowing that he clearly didn't understand about jurisdiction. He evidently didn't know that Universal Law trumps a location - with Common Law defined as: 'all people everywhere'. So, I granted him a fool's pass and said nothing.

My mood improved when one officer confirmed that his Mum was into chemtrails (those 'flying bird' droppings of toxic metals chaffed from above). If the vaccine metals don't get you then the aluminium, barium and strontium ones from the Manx aeroplanes will.

Then it was photo and DNA taking time. I was finally asked, "Non evidentially, what's all this about the Common Law Court?". I looked straight ahead and said nothing.

A big police fella (who turned out to be one, Andrew Lee) clearly didn't like the silence judging by his words, "Stay a c*nt then!". Hardly Shakespeare, granted, but likely he'd bunked off skool. One day he might realise I'm trying to save kids he may love, if he'd just push his pause - and entrapment - buttons.

I spent the night in a police cell.

On Saturday 13th July 2019 I was woken at 8.40am to go to 'court'. At the front desk of Douglas HQ the man in the uniform bagged up my possessions and showed me the contents list on screen. I again signed nothing. I was handcuffed, as was another fella in the waiting room, though fortunately not to each other. We were then joined by a younger man who clearly knew the process and liked to chat, a lot. That's saying something coming from me, granted.

I was offered an advocate to represent me (I should say re-present me legally but more of that later). I declined. The legal system uses word trickery more than can be easily grasped by the average per-son. In reality, the customer has no real understanding. So you 'stand-under' their words and their powers, if you don't know how they get one over you. What's the saying? ..."If you think knowledge is expensive, try ignorance". Again I was asked by a court official, "Do you want an advocate?". I shook my head and waved my hand, as in 'no', at their attempt to engage me in contract.

At 11.10am or so, I traipsed upstairs in to Douglas 'court'. Jayne Hughes, a high bailiff, was up at the pointy end of the ship. She was clearly aiming to be the captain that day and was on her game to steer me into dock. She asked me who I was. I wondered what yesterday had been about. I said nothing. She continued, "We cannot ascertain where you live and, as you are a serious flight risk, we will detain you at Jurby prison. Your demeanour in 'court' (by which she meant me not sitting when she 'commanded' me to) means I shall ask Jurby prison services to examine your mental health". Yeah, madness, twice in two days - the policeman and high bailiff must be sharing the same script and bonus payments. Now fully into her fee earning and commission stride she continued, "You will report to 'court' at 10am on Tuesday 16th July 2019 when, if you refuse to recognise the 'court', a plea of not guilty will be offered on your behalf for future appearance on the serious charges".

She then requested that I sit down as the charges were read out by the prosecutor; however, I remained standing as she had no authority nor jurisdiction. By not sitting, at her command, I was not granting her jurisdiction over me. The pro-secutor said I was 'identified' by my driving licence - which was strange, as I did not have one with me at the time of my unlawful arrest on 12th July. More transparent attempts at getting 'joinder'.

At Jurby prison I was allocated Cell 12, and it had a poor view and no pool. There were no welcome home cards on the mat, no flowers - not even a bowl of fresh fruit. But my name and number adorned the board at the doorway. The Officer called me by my christian name, pretty soon it would be 'wotcha mate' as we swapped holidays snaps and drank Chardonnay on the sun deck. Although small, the cell was self-contained but the bars cut out the light. Beyond the next block the fences stretched skywards, but at least they stopped anyone breaking in (and stealing the Chardonnay). I made up my bed as room service hadn't yet been round, which surprised me. At night, I turned the telly sound down to zero but left it on so, with the warm glow, the Officer could see I was 'alright'. I woke in the middle of the night but didn't know when. I'd decided at 60 years old never to wear a watch again, and seven hundred days into that time-fast I hadn't missed it.

Sunday 14th July Up with the lark, more so as it's Bastille Day - zut allors Jean Pierre! But unlike home there were no birds singing in the tree; prison silence was almost eerie. At 9am I had porridge for breakfast, hardly haute cuisine but it was all right - though no sign of honey and cream like at home. Before morning exercise I'm informed it's library day. As we exit F Wing an excitable spaniel appears with a prison officer on a lead, coincidentally, as we've vacated our cells. In a holding room we were are all searched and as my turn approached I said, "I do not consent" but I didn't resist as I was fresh out of tasers - but knew they might not be. In the library I selected three magazines (an October 2015 Health & Fitness and two Fortean Times) plus three books: 'The New Testament' by Beacon Bibles, 'Christian Science' by Mary Baker Eddy, and 'Booky Wooky 2' by Russell Brand. My choice surprised some of my new friends. I replied, "I like to dip in and out of stuff from saints to sinners". With Russell Brand twice winning shagger of the year I knew I'd get my money's worth. For the book hire in prison, same as Tammy Wynette sang, there was 'no charge'.

At 10.15am I was encouraged to have a shower as the skunks had spotted my underpants, just as had I... Officer Nixon asked about the smell - "Well Officer, they will just have to get used to it". The good officer also reminded me it was room cleaning day. Later, a fair array of forms appeared, including how to sign up to make calls to the outside world. The form confirmed that an automatic £2 credit had been added to my phone account at the time of reception. Wow, free money. You can also apply to do jobs within the prison, though 'safe-cracking for beginners' may be off limits.

At 11.50am it was time for lunch. My earliest ever 'lunch' by a country mile. I asked an officer if I could eat with the others for company (I wasn't Hannibal Lecter after all) but "No, not while you're in the induction phase" came the reply. Perhaps she thought I'd attack them with the crusty pie(?) of unknown origin. I'd rather take that than a chainsaw to a pub fight in Dartford.

This afternoon, judy was due to visit and she was seated at table 7. That was a first for us, in our 39 years. When she'd said 'yes' to: in sickness and in health, and for richer or poorer the vows had left out 'prison visit confirmation for your tosser of a husband'. But now was not the time for jokes.

She was stronger in mind than I had expected, although she had been frisked including 'open mouth' commands to ensure she wasn't carrying anything 'unusual'. For once, had they known, yes the sharpest thing she possessed would have been her tongue. Reserved for me, I'm sure.

At 3.30pm I had a visitation in my cell, as the God Squad arrived. The Catholic Priest was nice enough, but his transmitter has sucked the life blood out of his receiver crystals. Unfortunately the priest stood between me and the door. The Bible tells us: 'our Father has many rooms in his house' but I only had one cell door in mine - on F Wing. We both omitted to set our next appointment.

By mid afternoon it was time for a health review at Jurby prison. The young lady took blood and pulse measurements, and asked me various checklist questions. My answers were just about 'no' to every one of them. I declined the Hepatitis B vaccine (a liver wrecker) despite the young lady mentioning there were 'unhealthy' people in prison who might be doing blood (and other fluid) sharing activities. Not that I'd mentioned to her that I was hoping to have sex with Big Steve in D Block, just now. Nothing personal nor homophobic, since the thought-nazis ask.

By 5pm I was back in cell 12 again. I'd been given an 'Emergency Canteen' form to complete. I ordered a pack of four Crunchie bars, a childhood favourite; at just £1 for all four it seemed rude not to but by 9am on Weds 17th July they still hadn't arrived. Maybe there was thief in the prison?

Monday 15th July at 7.48am my personal valet called me for breakfast. The choice seemed to be: toast, toast and yet more toast. Clearly they hadn't heard of: 'no carbs before marbs' in the slammer. "Can I have porridge?". "No, that's only on Sunday" came the reply. So I grabbed alternative rations of: a tangerine and two 200ml cartons of full fat milk, and trundled off. At 8am I'd decided to dine alone as the door clanged shut. I'd packed away the candelabra and Steinway piano, but a yellow plastic chair can be kinda sexy. At 9.50am Officer Nixon said he would soon have to start removing things if I did not wish to sign the 'compact'.

Compact? Well, as I later found out, that is actually a contract, one 'capable of being enforced'...

"Well, I won't, so please take the telly - there's only dust on it".

Coming in with my breakfast, I noted my cell board had been amended. The 'obs 30 minutes' (short for observation, I reckoned) had been rubbed out - likely because they felt I was somewhat less in danger now, of rubbing myself out.

At midday I celebrated a new hour and delved into the sweaty crevices of 'Booky Wooky 2' by Russell Brand. If you can ignore the filth - and the shagger of the year antics - there are many lessons and fabulous lines. Russell seemed a lot like the late great comedian Peter Cook, "I've learnt from my mistakes and now I can repeat them exactly".

Later, the words of Mary Baker Eddy and 'Christian Science' beckoned. My Father was a big fan of hers - how strange that my Father was, stationed some 80 years ago in 1939, on Jurby airfield as a 17 year old; it's only taken a spell in jail to get me to read about a subject that he so valued. As Smooth Radio filled the airwaves, it was Gerry Rafferty's 'Baker Street' that cheered me up. Rumour has it he never licenced it for adverts despite some hugely obscene offers. Some things you simply can't put a price on. Like freedom, I thought. And decent Manx butter in prison.

Soon more forms arrived, this time white was out and green was in. One form had my spending limit of £26 and my wage of £5. Blimey this prison lark, "It's is an earner too, Terence". I might stay. It's the best way the Isle of Man government has ever found of bringing 'employment' to Jurby. I glanced wistfully out of the window - never had Snaefell looked so beguiling in the wispy distance, out across two 25 foot high fences and search lights, topped off with layers of razor wire. And the CCTV. The forms informed me that an alarm clock (large) was £11.99, and likely 2kg of Semtex was extra.

At 4.50pm it was time for evening dinner; clearly as late as they could make it. Pasta meat balls, followed by sponge pudding and custard, plus the bonus ball of a Wagon Wheel - a first in 50 years. I could feel the carbs were fattening me like a stuck pig in Lord of The Flies. Washed down with 200ml of full fat milk and a cupful of double cream. At 17.15 an officer came to take away the telly. My 'fault' as I'd not signed the compact to keep it.

Tuesday 16th July 2019. (no TV/radio/phone/alarm clock/watch). At 7.50am a 'court' man arrived or should that be 'curt' man? Twice I had asked him (politely) what time it was, and twice he said, "It's time". I'd even thrown a 'please' in there, at the right place, so it can't have been that. A good morning would have helped before they slapped the handcuffs on too.

I had made contact with friends and worked out my words. At 3pm I was called into 'court' before Jayne Hughes, 'high bailiff', once again. I did not sit when asked. Also when asked my name, I replied, "I am courtenay :heading a living man, I stand under the jurisdiction of the Common Law Court." To which she began, "MR HEADING...", and I spoke up, "IF you are referring to my legal fiction, I own my legal fiction". The high bailiff was not listening and duly replied, "I'm not interested in your legal fiction", she simply continued to lay out bail and other issues.

The pro-secutor passed in front of me with what they claimed was a facsimile of a DRIVING licence, but as that is of a fictitious person, I didn't view it with any interest. Nor did I speak. Later, the 'court' bailiff offered me an advocate but I said nothing - there was ice and entrapment in the air too.

Next up a Mr Woods, who I gather was an advocate, arrived in front of me but not at my request. As it was a 'be quiet day' I said nothing, while he whispered, "I can get you bail, I can help you". I kept looking straight ahead at the captain of the ship, but I remained on dry land. And mute. Finally, when they could take no more, I was asked to leave the 'court' two or three times.

Eventually on admonishment of the 'court helpers' I left the 'court'. Returning to a cell downstairs the young lady helper asked me if I needed an advocate. They sure must get a lot of commission. "No" I replied. A minute or two later a tall fella turns up, lowers the flap and asks, "Are you sure you don't need an advocate"? "No" sprang to my lips, as did "thank you".

A few minutes later (while Andy McNab's 'Exit Wound'

remained un-page-turned) advocate Ian Kermode arrives, more flap flapping of the door spy hole with the same 'offer' to contract. As he was now as keen as the rest to contract, he upped the offer still further, "I can help you, this is a relatively minor matter and we can get bail quickly" or some such. Andy McNab would have to kick the doors down on his own. I raised my hand, in a stop gesture, fearing that to speak would cost me 80 guineas, plus a stamp and three weeks' disbursements. He was clearly going for overtime now or had I tripped unwittingly into double bubble bonus time? So, licking my lips, the words 'NO!" finally forced their way out. He, no doubt, went off to prepare his invoice for 'attentive listening, one half day/or part thereof'. Plus VAT. And stamps.

Back at Jurby Prison around 6pm Officer Tim Russell popped round and luckily I was in for visitors. Especially one as nice as him. He listened intently to my medical monologue. We went through the 'compacts' which I signed (against my better judgement) such was his empathetic manner. Hats off to him.

Wednesday 17th July at 9.45am, another inmate who I'd paired up with at exercise times, stopped by and said cheerio, giving me a thumbs up - he was off to a new wing. A welcome gesture of support. If I'd been a horse I'm sure he'd have given me a stroke, and sugar lumps. Nice these prisoners.

At 12 noon on television Lord Peter Bottomley, former MP, recommended we all read the book, 'The Thin Blue Line' on police corruption - surely not? I was thinking. They'll be telling me next that Jimmy SaVILE is a 'wrong un' and that the BBC spent 30 years covering up paedophilia. At 3.50pm I was introduced to another nurse, just to see if I was a dangerous nutcase. We had a friendly chat and she seemed happy enough that I wasn't. At that moment in time.

I called jude to say: 'night night', but the time credits - rather than money on my account - ran out…

Channel 5's 'New GPs Behind Closed Doors' programme struck me that, blimey, everyone is so sick. GP to a guy in his 50's, "Do you smoke?". "Yes". "Do you get phlegm?". "Yes but just white phlegm". He continued, evidently on a (fag) roll, "My Mum & Dad have diabetes". Another GP was shown advising a 30's something Mum to get rid of her facial acne by using Roaccuatane... Eff me, NO......!!!! After all I've seen written up about it causing teenage suicides. A friend of mine in his 50's went near hallucinogenic while driving when he'd been using Roaccuatane. At least the GP was sort of on her game, warning "It can affect your mood and will harm your baby if you get pregnant, so use TWO forms of contraception". I've often found ugliness is the best contraceptive - this also saves tuppence three farthings on two condoms.

Thursday 18th July 7.39am, by the telly clock, and the warder came in, "They'll be coming for you soon for court". Later at 'court' with prisoner C. he said, "It's a full lock in day today and tomorrow for staff training. Food will be brought to you and there will be no exercise sessions". Dull and some.

I read over a fellow prisoner's notice of apology to 'court'. I don't think he'd been that long in school. As it was a court day I was really trying to concentrate - recalling it was Cal Washington of InPower Movement who'd said, "When you hire an advocate you've lost"... because their first duty is to the court. He also said the same about attending their court. John Smith of the Common Law Court, echoed, "You must not play in their sandpit either". Once there you will lose, it is how it is all designed.

Now that they had coerced me into 'identifying myself' they dropped the 'severe flight risk' b/s type theatricals. In any case, they likely knew their prison was full for business, plus I was drinking them out of full fat milk. At 11am give or take, I went upstairs to 'court'. I entered and spotted my friend, Russell, sat in a front row seat and, up at the bow of the ship, I noted one of the three magistrates was a lady I used to see out running over the hills when I lived down south. Result! And the chatter and court jestering hadn't even kicked off yet. This was a time for playing their 'legal' game - not a Lawful day. Our day would come later.

This time I was wearing long trousers. A surly prison officer had chucked me some grey jogging bottoms, as he'd deemed that shorts and trainers didn't quite pass scrutiny. I'm no fashion leader but I've still got the jogging bottoms as I believe no one should have to wear such sartorial, epic failure, items to court - the low bar food is bad enough without further humiliation.

After the court case I was free to go. Played their game with the entrapping name. I'd have said yes, I was Donald Duck if it got me out.

Prisoners lessons that I would take away forever:

Prisoners are mainly not scumbags. They are also friendly, surprisingly optimistic and most are honest as to why they find themselves in prison. The officers are generally nice too; some even watch Joe Rogan and the odd chemtrail exposé. The food is more than cut down to a budget and apparently has an extra 'ingredient' to take male urges away. Bowl, plate, cup, knife, fork and spoon are all provided. But room service gets a little irritated when you buzz them asking, "What do I do with the chicken bones from my dinner?", as the waste bin had no liner. So I wrapped them in loo roll before placing carefully in the bin. On mentioning the officer's irritation on the way to 'court' one day, a fellow prisoner said he flushed his dinner bones down the loo, one at a time - and it worked. Inventive bunch, and not just while knocking up blueprints of an iGlider and a carbon fibre vaulting pole.

I may have been on the receiving end of the legal system but, for certain, the Lawful process has only just begun for me... as an unpaid Common Law Advocate.

Oh, and by the way, in case you were wondering on all matters HPV, I did subsequently receive an official letter ('Our Ref: GR/SK040919') from Gary Roberts, chief constable, Isle of Man Police dated 6th September 2019 in which he wrote, 'I do not wish to meet you to discuss this matter and I can categorically inform you that the Constabulary will not be providing you with a crime reference number in respect of any deaths that you believe to have been caused by the vaccine'.

So, there you go...

12. Being well, eating well

The first wealth is health.
Ralph Waldo Emerson

In this final chapter of my book I thought I would share a little about my own approach to being healthy - to being Well.

Obviously this is my unique observation, the personal N=1 experiment of my life; for which I have to thank judy for an abundance of healthy food, and my love of sport.

Since a boy I've been competitive (and if the cap fits, combative) by nature. I'd initially expressed it in football, running, and throwing events. Moving on from soccer, I progressed to an hour of squash a day as well as running, and sometimes both on the same evening even after usually starting the day with 100 press-ups. For good measure. Energy and 'lack of' weren't words I knew back then - and still don't. To fuel all this activity food has always been a major part of my life. Friends holding parties used to quip, "If the three Heading brothers turn up there will be no food left for anyone else". If it came to elbowing and arm wrestling Granny over the finger buffet, I know who my money would be on.

After I left school, competitive running continued on the roads for nearly four decades at distances from 10 kilometres to the marathon; however, 5 to 10 miles was my best distance. In the beginning I loved cross country and trained regularly on Crowborough golf course. Many a golfer would wave their sticks (bats?) in the air to encourage me as I crossed their line of play. I couldn't hear what they called out but I'm sure some clearly thought I had no Father. Have no fear Captain, it's not a game I'll be taking up anytime soon. For me it lacks excitement, being as some say, 'a game played by men with small balls'. Although, of course, Tiger Woods might well disagree.

From 2012 I had been committed to completing the Parish Walk, the 85 mile annual walk around the Isle of Man in less than 24 hours. Slowly, I was learning how not to be sick while consuming 6,000 calories LESS than the 9,000 calories I'd burn during the walk. Gradually enzymes, digestion, salts, magnesium, hydration and food types really mattered. It was this experiment in the lab of life on foot which had me questioning, what is health? And, better, what is being well? The former seemed increasingly sick and expensive.

Having tried every piece of walking advice and footwear preparation known to man I wasn't sure I was winning; especially in the early years, when it was skin off the balls of the feet (and heels) and blood through the trainers. Proper blisters based on proper stupidity; however, the finish was all. Then an epiphany, or rather, I listened to a true walker. He suggested six things to keep blisters away and, ever since following his advice, they have. But medicine knows nothing of these tips. They keep recommending the daft things that I, too, used to do.

My journey to fitness had no input from doctors but with a Wife, the daughter of a farmer also down to her last 200 cookbooks - I kid you not. I was and remain blessed.

Loving natural foods I now also follow (religiously from mid January) the low carb high fat diet, as outlined by Jeff S. Volek PhD, RD and Stephen D. Phinney, MD, PhD in their book, 'The Art and Science of Low Carbohydrate Performance'. Counter-intuitively, it also had me walking 100 miles in under a day in August 2019 - with relative ease - in under 24 hours. In addition, and most importantly the 208,000 steps didn't cause me a single blister. Almost a walk in the park.

I only wish diets were called regimes instead and that fat wasn't such a feminist issue. Despite a 40 years print run Susie Orbach also laments how things have got worse not better. Sisters, 'start your avocado'. Fat and food, now we think of it, has gone from a feminist issue to one for all of us. It's a weighty subject for sure. Granted, it's not only the carbs that are complex.

As a fan of high fat 'Mediterranean' diets, what if they are not actually, in reality, artery cloggers? I'm rather partial to a plate of: cheese, avocado, olives, nuts, seeds, tomatoes, cucumber and courgette. The bonus balls being local onions and, not so local, cornichons, and peppers. Wait, it gets worse - all washed down with goats milk from an (little prick alert) unvaccinated goat herd. Maybe we already have a clue; the body makes fats and proteins but doesn't make carbs. Is that a big fat (non carb) clue?

What's important to correct (for many of us) is the lack of essential nutrients in modern, highly processed, inflammation causing diets. What if, to paraphrase Ronald Reagan, 'It's the unnatural sugars stupid'? Many health problems come from a lack of nutrients in the diet, as organs need all the colours and combos of un-denatured food. Witness, in enlightened hospitals they often give heart attack victims a high dose of magnesium (found in nuts, seeds and green leaf veg); but why wait until you're wired up to the mains getting some free electricity at 2am charging through your chest? Jump starting cars is infinitely more fun, Matron.

This, of course, is apart from the support needed for the unique frequency vibration of every internal organ.

The catchy saying is, 'one third of what you eat feeds you, two thirds feeds your doctor'. High fat diets may not work for everyone but they do work for the vast majority worldwide. They help our inbuilt physiology and enable fat dependent tribes to be less obese but work harder - and run faster come the Olympics.

The following is what works for my two legged laboratory - my own body, my Number = 1. Free at birth, thanks Mum. By focusing on my bod, I might delay when my number is finally up. My inevitable date with death and destiny. And less taxes.

I'm NO medic so I highly recommend you do your own research. I would suggest, though, not from the daily papers nor from the highly ranked (paid/sponsored links) search engine results. At the top. They say, 'when you're overweight you're overwhelmed'. From teenage to middle age we do something 30,000 times which has a major undeniable effect on our body. Yet doctors rarely start with the one essential question, what are you eating?. We have meals, three times a day for 10,000 days - yet, little of that behaviour is built around Wellness. So, the National 'Health' Service has to step in but ONLY when things go wrong. When the wheels come off your trolley you may end up on one of theirs, in a corridor, for four hours.

There is no pot of luck at the end of the rainbow or over the Pond either. The average US medic spends 21 hours (total) studying nutrition in four years at med school. Some of us do that in a week - certainly each month - and we still don't know that much.

Remember, humans are the only species who, when they think about 'diet', mean, 'I want to get into my bikini / mankini / trans-kini, on holiday'.

The brain is basically a fat (lipid) organ, and depriving it of natural fats restricts its ability to send electrical signals around the body from brain to toe. As sugar based diets have increased, so have diabetes, Alzheimer's (sometimes known as Type 3 diabetes) plus dementia - often inflammatory diseases

178

of clumpy cells. Or 'cell aggregation' if you've had years at med skool, and your wallet is $100,000+ less fat.

Diet seems a natural way to promote better health, or as lucky guesser Hippocrates said, "All dis-ease begins in the gut". But it is hard to avoid the normalised over-processed foods that are now so cheap and available 24/7, delivered by a kid on a moped. Our nutrient starved modern diet contributes significantly to the majority of chronic diseases often endured in later life.

Better still with fats, not only do they do more work - 9 calories of work per gram from fats versus only 4 calories per gram from carbs - fats are better at shouting, 'we're full!' at the brain. A simple experiment is to try eating one pound (in weight not money) of chocolate and one pound of cheese. Hardly science but certainly entertaining on a cold winter's night.

Here's a personal view of what works for me, my body and my trusty gut. I avoid - as much as possible - anything that comes in a tin or plastic. I avoid everything that says 'healthy' on it, especially 'low fat'. Low fat = high sugar. Those lab-coated inventors know how taste hijacks our logic and best interests.

Nature provides the healthiest packaging without added coatings or chemicals. I tend to eat 'good for me foods' eight days out of ten, to be able to have two 'nice for me' piggy days. A regime shouldn't be a strict dietary chore.

Breakfast: Three days a week. My 'Dutch' breakfast (Dutch men are the tallest in the world - maybe their diet helps): eggs, Manx kippers or cheese as the protein element. Plus: pickled onions, olives, peppers, lettuce, pumpkin & chia seeds, cucumber and tomatoes with whole grain toast liberally buttered - no industrial 'healthy marg' nor low fat spreads. Ever.

Often I'll have poached eggs with avocado on buttered toast (both local). Sometimes my regime is: eggs, sausage, mushrooms with tomatoes cooked in butter. Occasionally, I'll have porridge plus nuts, seeds, grapes, honey and coconut oil. A weekend treat is smoked salmon (it's loaded with Omega 3 brain food) and scrambled eggs cooked with cream, plus slices of avocado. Breakfast time varies, from doing an airport run at 5am to a mid morning brunch.

We're not programmed for regular food - so every Monday is my fasting day.

Lunch, side plate (if anything?): Local cheese, nuts, raisins, seeds, tomatoes, cucumber - or just a banana some days. I always eat an apple a day - believing (and hoping) it still keeps the doctor away. Snack on: grapes, cherries, banana, peaches, maybe a grapefruit sweetened with local, not blended, honey.

Dinner: Some meat/local lamb, or local fish (oily or otherwise) sometimes with an 'all colours' salad, more often with lots of: broccoli, asparagus, peppers, onions, garlic, carrots. Occasionally (meat free trigger alert) a 'veggie' dinner, haloumi cheese & vegetables cooked in coconut oil or butter. A recent favourite is sweet potato/yam full of vitamin A with a few un-denatured carbs.

I drink plenty of water with a good squeeze of lemon/lime in it. That took a million deaths of sailors to catch on, scurvy avoiders that we all now are. Full fat cream and local honey sweetens three cups of morning coffee - my big vice. A regular green tea too with (moo alert) whole fat milk.

I also have a fair bit of fruit (but not processed juice as it's too high in sugar - the lack of fibre means the sugars are released too quickly in the gut).

I'm a big fan of walking plus regular press-ups to delay the onset of bingo wings and to keep my spine and joints strong. On Tuesday evenings it's time for Hot Yoga to sweat out the toxins. When I remember I also do 'the plank' for core strength, plus some stretches.

Turning fat to muscle helps the metabolism burn more energy as fuel. It's said the body has around 100,000 calories of fat stored energy within it and fat burns more effectively than sugars; BUT keeping it 'ketosis ready' is the key bit.

Maybe a Wellness diet would help to regain those recently lost 'doctor free days' as we age. Weighing yourself seems an odd number because as we age we lose muscle - as we head towards death.

If that sharp knifed surgeon wants to whip out your gall bladder he/she may not have mentioned, "If you lack a gall bladder you'll have a greater incidence of colon cancer and runny poo, and less ability to break down essential fats in future". After all, are we really designed with excess organs?

With 65% of biopsies nowadays being taken in the gastrointestinal tract, maybe it's my diet doc? Now there's a mad thought, one that's not quite mainstream yet.

We are often over fed but, in recent decades, under-nourished. The body compensates by storing - as fat - our modern hi-carb/sugar based diets, to prepare us for an assumed famine.

Modern diets often lack: sodium, potassium, zinc, magnesium, calcium, vitamins B, C, D, and iron, while (to me) we have wrongly demonised natural, healthy, fats. Too much of some molecules block absorption of others, whilst processed food diets lead to poor bone, heart & system health. Blood or urine tests are often irrelevant, as the bodily 'symphony' seeks every instrument to play in tune but does not always show up in a blood or breath test.

Unbiased 'functional medicine' is more of a challenge as the needs of our body change, with time. Taking in hormones unnaturally and bottles of vitamins C or D, don't seem to help too much, while The Sun is naturally our friend. Yet, increasingly, we lack sunlight/vitamin D and make it worse by use of sunscreens. Whole food nutrients likely beat pills every time.

Perhaps we should have a new mantra, 'you are the captain of your own ship'; whereas the current medical model is one where a physician flies your plane, while he or she sits out of harms way on the ground.

Apple cider vinegar with water before bed, helps aid overnight digestion & gut microbiome - said also to reduce possible kidney stones and gall bladder problems. The biggest benefit of apple cider vinegar is triggering (fat burning) 'hunter gatherer times' ketones.

In preference, I also don't tend to drink during meals - unless at social events. Water is best drunk well before or after a meal, to enable strong stomach acids to comprehensively digest food without dilution. The next stages of nutrient assimilation are best done without fiddling with nature, without glugging any water, cola or exotic beverages. Your gut juices will be especially compromised by unnatural liquids and, as evidence is showing, ant-acid proton pump inhibitor medicine.

If you can sort the gut you'll sort your body and mind.

Ensure you get daily fresh air, vital for vitamin D (the master hormone) but also look to avoid chemicals in the home, such as: toxic scented candles, flame retardants, strong detergents, after shaves and perfumes - all, I believe, are endocrine disrupters. Plus 'cleansing' fluids for nail polish and many 'beauty' products.

182

I most certainly ignore the Public Health England standard approved diet, it being: carb heavy & 'fat light' (fat is an essential cellular / membrane builder for adding muscle). But refined carbs / glyphosated grains / sugars are certainly everywhere and pushed hard by Big Food. So, carry nuts/seeds around in a bag for when your craving starts. In time, with changed habits, the body will become fat expectant not carb dependent, and return to its natural balance.

Anyone who says the science is 'settled' should be politely reminded (as a sick society) that it isn't - that's more a definition of an unchanging religion.

Any eating regime should be modified over time to reflect and compensate for aging. In my mind, natural aging is good; the alternative, though, sucks.

I went a walkin' recently with a good friend and, as it was a long one, we covered just about every topic going under the hot sun. We're both fans of the HFLC (high fat & low carb) eating regime, when up popped discussion of a dietary inhibitor. That inhibitor being soy beans and their 'under the radar' lectins. It seems lectins are highly concentrated plant proteins found in many legumes - soy cleverly uses them to protect against their natural predators.

Fermented or sprouted soy is, in reality, good for us.

Unfermented soy, in the quantities currently eaten, is leading to gut, goiter and other harms. Processed soy blocks nutrient absorption by interfering with proper food digestion. It's been linked to cognitive fogging, immune system dysfunction and cancers. Since the 1990's, GMO (Genetically Modified Organism) soy makes up 90% of all US grown soy and is also correlated as causing: low birth weight babies and, later, excessive weight gain. Scary, and yet another ingredient to add to the list of foodstuffs that 'might just kill you'. Slowly.

A bit like life - all this will end in death; so let's dig deeper to see if we should fully sling the soy, boy...

Soy, as mentioned, are legumes - a type of bean (a pulse when dried) - and as many a good product they originated in the Far East. Another one of Asia's best products, of course, being the Honda motorbike. But what if soy is actually less fun and more dangerous - over time - than some of Honda's two wheeled finest? What if soy is actually taking us for a bit of a ride, too?

What about soy milk, I hear you ask - that staple of the newest generation of (trigger alert) veganistas everywhere? Apparently, soy milk is made by soaking and grinding soy beans, boiling the mixture and filtering out the remaining particles. With soy milk being 'non animal', many see it as a non dairy milk alternative. But 'GMO soy' is absent in the listed soy milk ingredients; strictly too scary, so it's kept 'off label'.

Soy, it seems, messes with your leptin receptors, those hunger regulators - the software of the 'I've had enough, thanks' on the gut brain superhighway. (I thought that was ghrelin but, there you go, another pub quiz tie-breaker that I'll lose).

When marketing gets involved the trumpet players' tune will belt out the latest 'must have' super food - riding to our rescue over the horizon, along with John Wayne. But what if soy is actually, a bit, all: Big Hat, No Cattle?

Soy contains isoflavones, raising your oestrogen levels while competing with, and lowering, your body's testosterone. Over time (multiple meal times that is) increased ingestion of adulterated soy sees your energy and libido decline, while gynecomastia increases. I might have boobed with that last one guys - but I really don't think so.

What if we're a bit asleep at the dietary wheel? What if soy is more: stupor food, than super food? Soy snuck onto the 'staples list' a couple of decades ago, but what if the US version, now regularly crossing the Pond, is, via proteins, genetically modifying us too? Tested in the lab for weeks, yet there is now decades long harms as evidenced in brains, and showing up on hips, bellies, and breasts everywhere...

Finally, we have to ask: when is a toy boy not a toy boy? When it's a soy boy. It's an adolescent physical change we increasingly need to keep abreast of, sadly. One that needs an honest and open debate with moobs man.

Beyond the issue of soy, it seems the World is steadily going natural botanicals, while applying some clinical rigour alongside a little gentle tree hugging. How better, ultimately, than to combine the process and distribution of Big Pharma with a recognition that plants are the basis of almost all the medicines in widespread use today? Plants to which they add a little something, so they can be patented.

Nature has some blood pressure lowering plants, such as hibiscus, which acts as a diuretic to draw sodium from the bloodstream, to decrease pressure on the arterial wall.

Another plant (but from the garlic family) is turmeric (curcuminoids) which has been used to treat a variety of internal disorders for millennia, from skin infections and colds, through to treat liver complaints. Both Cancer Research UK and the University of Maryland have some promising study results that curcumin may help treat cancers, and also ulcerative colitis. As ulcerative colitis is a chronic disease of the digestive tract (where 2/3rds of all biopsies are performed) that may make it a welcome addition to the natural remedy arsenal.

The gut is called the second brain for great reason, the two should act in sync just as Nature designed us.

Giulia Enders has an unusual fascination, one not dialled out of her by polite society, and it shows in her book: GUT. From bacteria to energetic enzymes, along the way she also steps into poo; that little discussed but vital chemical dumping ground - a barometer of our daily performance - but one with less wind due in from The Azores, hopefully.

Within two hours of our birth, apparently, gut bacteria have spawned five further generations. Nature does that every 20 minutes to help us digest everything from breastmilk to burgers. Then there's the sphincters; those non return valves at the top and bottom ends of our digestive pipework, with the stomach the vital holding tank, in between. The sphincter valves can even reverse their role when the system software shouts "quick, vomit".

Our mouths too, commanded by the gut brain axis, support vomit veneration by flooding our teeth with saliva to protect their enamel from strong stomach acids coming up. Our body is truly majestic, if we dare think about it.

Smooth muscles keep things moving silently along within us, whilst seeking no medals, praise nor standing ovation. Around us, our personal microbial 'signature' is on everything from our patted dog to our computer keyboard, making them uniquely 'ours'. Studying the gut is a scientific frontier, ever more vital with the rash of compromised immune systems and food intolerances among certain groups of us.

Things have clearly changed Granddad. We don't need to raise a stink about poo at private dinner parties, even if all the lessons of life may not smell as sweet as a rose - and Giulia certainly does a great job in lifting the lid on that.

Is it too potty-mouthed to ask why increasing numbers of small people, called children, have so much gut, lung and brain dysfunction? Maybe not, if they're being fed a 'diet' of tainted food and tainted meds.

Einstein liked asking questions... in his memory we should too.

It is a universal truth that all things that begin must end.

And so, I will finish here.

Be Well.

courtenay-adam-lawrence :heading

Postscript

People in 'The System' may try to silence me, as has happened to numerous others who have been prepared to speak out where they saw injustice, but I guarantee: I will not stop.

So, for those of you who have managed to stick with me, and read through to the end of this book, I congratulate you.

My hope and wish is that along the way you have had your eyes and mind opened a little more than before you started reading it. And had at least one laugh, too.

To say there are many troubles at this time is somewhat of an understatement, but more and more people are waking up, being courageous in making a stand, and speaking to Truth.

If each one of us does our own little bit - in our own ways - we will make this world a better place.

'You are your own Devil, you are your own God,
You've fashioned the paths your footsteps have trod,
And no-one can save you from error nor sin,
Until you have listened to the Spirit within.'

(part of the beautiful Maori poem, 'My Law,'
written in the 18th century by Tieme Ranapiri)

With Love. Be Well.

courtenay-adam-lawrence :heading

Common Law Advocate

20/02/2020

Appendix

Disclaimer:

As with everything I say, I recommend you to please do your own research on any of the topics I have mentioned in the book.

I remind you that I am not giving 'medical' or 'legal' advice in this book and, as such, the book is considered 'purely for entertainment purposes only'.

Bearing that in mind, I do encourage you to watch:
Monty Python - You don't vote for Kings! (3 mins):
https://www.youtube.com/watch?v=H_Jb2gqu5xw

There follows an assorted selection of resources - videos, papers, articles and books - which you can investigate and check out for yourselves.

By doing so, you will be more informed and educated than a great number of (so called) 'professionals'.

Chapter 3. Moving on and waking up

Dr David Healy, FDA presentation - 'David Healy Antidepressant Testimony' December 2006 (3 mins):
https://www.youtube.com/watch?v=VjXDDMK-Awg

Dr David Healy, Keyll Darree, Nobles Hospital, Isle of Man presentation - 'Is Science Authoritative? Authorship & Authority' 19th May 2017 (76 mins):
https://www.youtube.com/watch?v=9QYpoal_Fzk&t

Dr Waney Squier- 'A Call for More Scrutiny in Cases of Shaken Baby Syndrome TEDxWandsworth' (17 mins):
https://www.youtube.com/watch?v=O5FyTFs7P7U

Andy Burnham, The 'Factor 8 Scandal' - 'Negligence of a very serious kind' - MP Andy Burnham (3 mins):
https://www.youtube.com/watch?v=bLRhUwHSqlk

Chapter4. Going deeper in to the mire

Aseem Malhotra, 'Big Food and Big Pharma killing for profit?' (11 mins):
https://www.youtube.com/watch?v=aNM7L4YQfCY

and

'Profit over Population Health, at The European Parliament', Aseem Malhotra, and Sir Richard Thompson, (125 mins):
https://www.youtube.com/watch?v=jcnd3usdNxo

Chapter 5 Statins to start

'Statins 'The Known Unknowns' By Prof Sherif Sultan' (35 mins):
https://www.youtube.com/watch?v=xim_BDMwaFg

$tatin Nation, The Great Cholesterol Cover-Up
'STATIN NATION First 13 mins' (13 mins):
https://www.youtube.com/watch?v=mNDqtZWbSpM

Paper: The benefits of high cholesterol, Dr Uffe Ravnskov, MD, PhD:
http://www.ravnskov.nu/2015/12/30/the-benefits-of-high-cholesterol/

Paper: The Hunt 2 Study, Dr Malcolm Kendrick:
https://drmalcolmkendrick.org/tag/hunt-2/

Chapter 6. HPV vaccine carnage

'HPV: Uninformed Consent' - 348 US deaths (in 2017) after HPV vaccines, Alliance for Natural Health (6 mins): https://www.youtube.com/watch?v=aHf17TSgYww

'Sacrificial Virgins (part 1 of 3) Not For The Greater Good' (12 mins): https://www.youtube.com/watch?v=KAzcMHaBvLs

Paper: Patient Information Leaflet for Gardasil 9: https://www.medicines.org.uk/emc/product/7330/pil

'Mr Speaker - Juan Watterson - hosting public debate on HPV vaccine harms' 14th Aug 2018 (103 mins): https://vimeo.com/286917088

Manx TV call for public debate, 2nd November 2018 (10 mins): https://www.youtube.com/watch?v=3pT8gELuycY

Paper: Matthew Mold, and Christopher Exley - Aluminium in Brain Tissue in Autism Spectrum Disorder: https://www.sciencedirect.com/science/article/pii/S0946672X17308763

Paper: Professor Chris Exley - The brain and toxic aluminium exposure - since 1984 (Orwell would be proud!): https://www.hippocraticpost.com/paediatrics/infants-are-uniquely-vulnerable-to-aluminium-in-vaccines/

Dr Sherri Tenpenny - 'What If You Had Known?' 4th Dec 2018 (98 mins): https://vimeo.com/313117294

Dr Sherri Tenpenny, interview with Del Bigtree, The Highwire, 'No Evidence' - The Truth about Gardasil, 24th Jan 2020 (128 mins):
https://www.youtube.com/watch?v=YLri0CXoflU

WHO, Global Vaccine Safety Summit with Dr Heidi Larson, MA Phd & Dr Soumya Swaminathan 'CAUGHT ON CAMERA: W.H.O Scientists Question Safety Of Vaccines' 3rd Dec 2019 (9 mins):
https://www.youtube.com/watch?v=s2IujhTdCLE

Vaccine film: A Shot in the Dark (2020 Documentary)
Dr Stanley Plotkin, MD (leading authority in vaccinology, 'The Godfather of Vaccines') is featured in this film. (33 mins);
https://www.youtube.com/watch?v=B2N35yVQcSk

The following video is eye-opening: 'Stanley Plotkin, Godfather of Vaccines, Under Oath' (7 mins):
https://www.youtube.com/watch?v=fr_o_XXoJ3M

Watch Actual Proceedings for Vaccine Approval in JUST four Minutes - 'Proof vaccines are NOT tested properly before approval':
https://www.youtube.com/watch?v=L_JJMpe00mM

SaneVax: Promoting only Safe, Affordable, Necessary & Effective vaccines and vaccination practices through education and information.
https://sanevax.org/media-about-sanevax/about/

Ongoing survey in Germany - vaccine versus unvaccinated study:
https://www.vaccineinjury.info/survey/results-unvaccinated/results-illnesses.html

Chapter 7. Catching on to cancer

Peter Glidden, 'Chemotherapy Does NOT Work 97% of The

Time' (5 mins):
https://www.youtube.com/watch?v=5sJFyEDGpG4

Paper: Dr Richard J Ablin - PSA Test Is Misused, Unreliable:
https://www.medscape.com/viewarticle/828854_7

The Crisis of Science, Corbett Report 2019 (31 mins):
https://www.youtube.com/watch?v=KDjadDoze10

Dr Stefanie Seneff, Presentation on harmful effect of glyphosate, October 2013, "Roundup, The Elephant In The Room" (56 minutes):
https://www.youtube.com/watch?v=MqWwhggnbyw

Dr Véronique Desaulniers, 'The 7 Essentials', (4 mins):
https://www.youtube.com/watch?v=VFuLFYoWUtE

and

'Busting Through Cancer Myths with Dr Véronique Desaulniers' (36 mins):
https://www.youtube.com/watch?v=mCtAvVslCk4

Chapter 8. Follow the money

Big Business Lobbying:
https://www.opensecrets.org/news/2019/10/big-pharma-continues-to-top-lobbying-spending/

'Why the majority is always wrong - Paul Rulkens - TEDxMaastricht' October 2014, (11 mins):
https://www.youtube.com/watch?v=VNGFep6rncY

Autism: The Next Great Depression - $1 trillion autism epidemic, Del Bigtree, The Highwire, with Political Economist Toby Rogers, PhD MPP Jan 2020 (91 mins):
https://www.youtube.com/watch?v=BzYZwiJNX-0

Chapter 10. Considering Common Law

Strawman, (5 mins):
https://www.commonlawcourt.com/aiovg_videos/meet-your-strawman/

Kevin Annett, let Kanata speak - 'Who is Kevin Annett?' (47 mins):
https://www.youtube.com/watch?v=AY4h3hDjOYM

Common Law, John Harris: 'The truth is simple, mankind makes it complicated', filmed in 2009 (53 mins):
https://www.youtube.com/watch?v=PNyhV46AzjI

'Natural Person vs Artificial Person' - From 2013 (8 mins):
https://www.youtube.com/watch?v=9qW55yEYSyw

Chapter 11. Who is the criminal?

Arrest video tynwald day, 5th July 2019 - 'Courtenay Heading HPV Vaccine Yellow Vest tynwald day' (23 mins):
https://www.youtube.com/watch?v=h_Nb2Zi3Gf0

Chapter 12. Being well, eating well

The Obesity Fix, the science of food and weight Part 1:
https://www.anhinternational.org/2018/03/15/the-obesity-fix-part-1/

and

The drug free obesity fix, Part 2:
https://www.anhinternational.org/2018/03/22/the-drug-free-obesity-fix-video/

Cardiologist, Dr Aseem Malhotra, Sugars and Fats explained:
http://www.menshealth.co.uk/food-nutrition/the-truth-about-fat-and-sugar-is-finally-explained

Dr Mark Hyman on Eating Fat to Get Healthy interview with Lewis Howes, 2016 (56 mins):
https://www.youtube.com/watch?v=xgWBKJsJtk0

Wellness - A new health model for the Isle of Man
25th June 2019 (88 mins):
https://www.youtube.com/watch?v=kT3hiVe1NMA

⟨⟩ ⟨⟩ ⟨⟩

Books (listed in alphabetical order)

A Statin Nation: Damaging Millions in a Brave New Post-health World
Dr Malcolm Kendrick
(27 December 2018) - 320 Pages - ISBN 9781786068255

Dissolving Illusions: Disease, Vaccines, and The Forgotten History
Suzanne Humphries MD, Roman Bystrianyk
(27 July 2013) - 532 Pages - ISBN 9781480216891

Fats That Heal, Fats That Kill: The Complete Guide to Fats, Oils, Cholesterol, and Human Health
Udo Erasmus
(01 December 1993) - 456 Pages - ISBN 9780920470404

Gardasil. Faith and propaganda versus hard evidence
Nicole Delépine, Gérard Delépine
(04 April 2019) - 210 Pages - ISBN 9791030202892

Gardasil: Fast Tracked & Flawed
Helen Lobato
(01 September 2017) - 140 Pages - ISBN 9781742199931

How to End the Autism Epidemic: Revealing the Truth About Vaccines
J.B. Handley
(26 September 2018) - 208 Pages - ISBN 9781603588249

Illuminati Agenda 21: The Luciferian Plan To Destroy Creation
Dean and Jill Henderson
(05 June 2018) - 153 Pages - ISBN 9781720819103

Lipitor Thief of Memory
Duane Graveline
(01 November 2006) - 196 Pages - ISBN 9781424301621

Plague of Corruption: Restoring Faith in the Promise of Science
Kent Heckenlively, Judy Mikovits
(14 April 2020) - 272 Pages - ISBN 9781510752245

Plague: One Scientist's Intrepid Search for the Truth about Human Retroviruses and Chronic Fatigue Syndrome (ME/CFS), Autism, and Other Diseases
Kent Heckenlively, Judy Mikovits
(09 March 2017) - 464 Pages - ISBN 9781510713949

Shattered Dreams: The HPV Vaccine Exposed
Miss Christina England BA Hon
(21 May 2019) - 724 Pages - ISBN 9781976088711

The Art and Science of Low Carbohydrate Performance
RD, Jeff S. Volek PhD, PhD, Stephen D. Phinney MD
(01 April 2012) - 172 Pages - ISBN 9780983490715

The Biology of Belief: Unleashing the Power of Consciousness, Matter & Miracles
Bruce H Lipton
(11 October 2016) - 312 Pages - ISBN 9781401952471

The Body Electric
Robert O. Becker, Gary Selden
(01 November 1998) - 368 Pages - ISBN 9780688069711

The Great Cholesterol Con
Dr Malcolm Kendrick
(07 July 2008) - 288 Pages - ISBN 9781844546107

The Great Prostate Hoax: How Big Medicine Hijacked the PSA Test and Caused a Public Health Disaster
Richard J. Ablin, Ronald Piana
(04 March 2014) - 272 Pages - ISBN 9781137278746

The HPV Vaccine On Trial: Seeking Justice for a Generation Betrayed
Mary Holland, Kim Mack Rosenberg, Eileen Iorio
(18 October 2018) - 512 Pages - ISBN 9781510710801

The Peanut Allergy Epidemic: What's Causing It and How to Stop It
Heather Fraser
(06 June 2017) - 256 Pages - ISBN 9781510726314

Too Many Pills: How Too Much Medicine is Endangering Our Health and What We Can Do About It
Dr James Le Fanu
(24 May 2018) - 320 Pages - ISBN 9781408709771

The Vaccine-Friendly Plan: Dr. Paul's Safe and Effective
Approach to Immunity and Health-from Pregnancy Through
Your Child's Teen Years
Paul Thomas M.D., Jennifer Margulis Ph.D
(23 August 2016) - 448 Pages - ISBN 9781101884232

Vaccines: Making the Right Choice for Your Child
Richard Halvorsen
(26 October 2017) - 304 Pages - ISBN 9781783340958

Whistle in the Wind: Life, death, detriment and dismissal in
the NHS. A whistleblower's story
Peter Duffy
(24 July 2019) - 264 Pages - ISBN 9781082231964

You can contact me via:

courtenay@manx.net

or

courtenay@jurbywellness.im

website:
www.jurbywellness.im

Forthcoming Books Schedule

The four part trilogy from

courtenay-adam-lawrence :heading

Provisional launch dates:

Wednesday 1st April 2020:

From Health Heretic To Common Law Advocate

Peering inside the edge of a rabbit hole, medicine isn't quite what it seems. The animal experiments really are more rabid dog than cuddly kitten; but what about their rights? Just as importantly, what about our rights as we live on a tax farm? This book may furrow the legal brow - as we gain a basic grasp of Common Law and the coming remedies.

Wednesday 11th November 2020:

Common Law Common Sense

"Well, guvnor, this Common Law is all Dutch to me" said the Barista lawyer; but he was only skooled in legalese. If only he stayed on for a decent dose of Latin and Common Law. So there's a parallel word system: a soul and a sole; a seaman and a semen. We're soon to realise that 'court' hearings should be called 'spellings', and that the paper charges are the 'court'.

Thursday 1st April 2021:

The Emperor Has No HPV Vaccines

The Medical Mafia knows no shame; those who will stop at nothing to profitably: vaccinate any woman or man (soon baby too?) to allegedly guard against what used to be a rare disease of older women. With HPV vaccine deaths and harms in 55 Countries, how can society be so flippant over such medically induced carnage? Let's draw a deep breath as I share evidence of true science. Meanwhile, at the younger end of the scale, we note the 30.6% fall in the number of registered births on the Isle of Man in the last 10 years (Manx independent 30th January 2020). However, we have been here before with: vaccine-induced provocation polio, smallpox-induced meningitis and 'herd immunity' measles epidemics. Or even the latest must-have, false-flag, weaponised, viral pandemic. Yes, really.

Friday 1st April 2022:

We Need To Talk about 12 Conspiracy Realities

Forget about Kevin, we really need to talk about conspiracy realities. We need a sharp focus to deep dive, to ask with a pointy finger - is there actually something to see here, afterall, guys? Why should we 'move along' when magic bullets zigzag, strong buildings fall straight down, and nice people trip over the cat - who it turned out was armed. Our governments do love us really. Is it actually atishoo of lies pointing to (man-dated) flu vaccination activating coronaviruses? In evidence for those truly woke-ing up we will look at the patent holders of the Coronavirus (COVID-19) which may yet cause a right royal stink. Currency reset, Mr Pirbright? Maybe more The Eyes of Darkness... truth be told.